NATURAL
BATH & SPA

NATURAL
BATH & SPA

MAKE YOUR OWN SOAPS, CREAMS, LOTIONS AND OILS

Cheryl Coutts and Ada Warren

NEW HOLLAND

FOR ANDREW

First published in 2004 by
New Holland Publishers (UK) Ltd
London · Cape Town · Sydney · Auckland

Garfield House, 86–88 Edgware Road, London W2 2EA, United Kingdom
www.newhollandpublishers.com

80 McKenzie Street, Cape Town 8001, South Africa

Level 1, Unit 4, 14 Aquatic Drive, Frenchs Forest, NSW 2086, Australia

218 Lake Road, Northcote, Auckland, New Zealand

ISBN 1 84330 697 2

Senior Editor: Clare Sayer
Production: Hazel Kirkman
Design: Isobel Gillan
Photographer: Shona Wood
Editorial Direction: Rosemary Wilkinson

10 9 8 7 6 5 4 3 2 1

Reproduction by Modern Age Repro, Hong Kong
Printed and bound by Times Offset (M)) Sdn Bhd, Malaysia

CONTENTS

INTRODUCTION

Life is often hectic and tiring, stress is never far away, but we should all make time for special treats, and the bathroom is the perfect place to start. Bath time can be a great "switch-off-and-relax time", a time for pampering the body and mind. It was with this daily wind-down in mind that we began making our own soaps, and because we couldn't find products in the shops that fulfilled our needs for moisturizing, therapeutic and exquisitely aromatic products. Making your own soap and other items for the bath and spa, including creams, shampoos, massage oils and shave lotions, allows you to use natural products, such as essential oils, to achieve an overall feeling of well-being, as well as pampering the skin and the senses. In this book we have collected a number of our favourite recipes for you to try for yourself.

This book features recipes for all times of the day and all members of the family. There are treats for the shower, because there is nothing better than a morning boost to leave you delicately fragranced and ready to meet the world head-on, while our night creams will work their magic while you sleep. There are shampoos for the children and plenty of soaps, creams and shave products for the men in the family. There are lotions to use from top to toe, and even recipes that target specific complaints, such as varicose veins or sunburn.

What's more, none of these recipes will leave you smelling like you've been sprayed by every perfume seller on the ground floor of a department store. This is because essential oils, which are used to fragrance and give identity to each recipe, have a gentle, natural aroma that will soothe you and those around you.

We both love growing our own fresh herbs, which we use in our soapmaking as well as in our cooking. We make soap like we cook, because we love it, and our friends and family are willing guinea pigs for all our new inventions. We hope that you will have as much fun as we do as you work your way through this book. None of the recipes are difficult, so don't be scared to try them. And once you have got the hang of the various processes and the qualities of each essential oil, you can adapt our recipes to suit your own tastes and needs.

BASIC INFORMATION

A HISTORY OF SOAP AND BATHING

The origins of personal cleanliness date back to prehistoric times. Since water is essential for life, the earliest people lived near water and knew something about its cleansing properties; at least that it rinsed the mud off their hands.

A soap-like material found in clay cylinders during the excavation of ancient Babylon is evidence that soapmaking was known as early as 2800BC. Inscriptions on the cylinders suggest that fats were boiled with ashes to make soap. Records also show that ancient Egyptians bathed regularly. The Ebers papyrus, a medical document from about 1500BC, describes the process of mixing animal fats, vegetable oils and alkaline salts to form a soap, used for washing and treating skin diseases.

The early Greeks bathed for aesthetic reasons, and apparently did not use soap. Instead, they cleaned their bodies with blocks of clay, sand, pumice and ashes, then anointed themselves with oil and scraped off the oil and dirt with a metal instrument known as a *strigil*.

As Roman civilization advanced, so did bathing. The first of the Roman baths, supplied with water from aqueducts, was built in about 312BC. The baths were luxurious, and bathing became very popular. Soap acquired its name, according to Roman legend, from Mount Sapo, where animals were sacrificed. Rain washed a mixture of melted animal fat and wood ashes down into the clay soil along the Tiber River. Women found that this mixture cleaned their washing with less effort.

After the fall of Rome in 467AD, and the resulting decline in bathing habits, much of Europe felt the impact of filth upon public health. The lack of personal cleanliness contributed heavily to the great plagues of the Middle Ages and it wasn't until the 17th century that bathing started to come back into fashion in much of Europe. However, in other parts of the medieval world personal cleanliness remained important. Daily bathing was a common custom in Japan during the Middle Ages, and in Iceland pools warmed with water from hot springs were popular gathering places.

Soapmaking was an established craft in Europe by the 7th century. Soapmaking guilds guarded their trade secrets closely. Gradually more varieties of soap became available for shaving and shampooing, bathing and laundering. Italy, Spain and France were early centres of soap manufacturing, due to the ready supply of raw materials such as olive oil. The English began making soap during the 12th century. For many years soapmaking remained, essentially, a household chore. Eventually, professional soapmakers began collecting waste fats from households, in exchange for some soap. A major step towards large-scale commercial soapmaking occurred in 1791 when a French chemist, Nicholas Leblanc, patented a process for making soda ash, or sodium carbonate, from common salt. Caustic soda, or soda ash, is the alkali obtained from ashes that combines with fat to form soap. The Leblanc process yielded quantities of good quality, inexpensive caustic soda.

Well into the 19th century soap was heavily taxed as a luxury item by many countries. When the high tax was removed, soap became available to ordinary people, and cleanliness standards improved throughout the world.

Scientific discoveries over the last 200 years have made soapmaking one of the world's fastest growing industries. At the same time, its broad availability changed soap from a luxury item to an everyday necessity.

PRINCIPLES OF SOAPMAKING

Making soap is really quite straightforward and can be lots of fun. Quite simply, soap is created when an oil, or combination of oils, which are usually acid, is mixed with an alkaline solution of sodium hydroxide (caustic soda) and water, otherwise known as lye water. The chemical reaction that occurs is known as "saponification". There follows a breakdown of the basic soapmaking stages, using what is known as the "cold process" method. This is the science behind the process, and you will find the necessary detailed instructions in each recipe, or in the basic techniques section on page 18.

Weighing and measuring
The recipes in this book dictate the exact amount of ingredients to use, that is the oils, caustic soda and mineral water. The correct proportion of oil to lye water is a crucial factor in the soapmaking process.

Saponification
This is the chemical process that occurs when the oils and lye water are mixed. Over the curing process (see below) the alkali in the lye water is neutralized, so although soap is made with sodium hydroxide (caustic soda), once cured, it does not contain it.

pH balance
This is the measure of the acidity or alkalinity of a substance. The skin is slightly acid at a pH of 5.5, and most cold process soaps are between pH8 and 9. This can be measured using a litmus paper, and any soap reading above pH10 should be discarded, because it is too alkaline. Some commercial soaps have their alkalinity reduced artificially to make them "neutral", but the chemicals used to do this probably make the soaps worse to wash with than a more alkaline soap.

Tracing
Tracing is the term used to describe the point at which the mixture has been stirred and thickened adequately, when a little of the soap drizzled over the surface of the mixture leaves a line or "trace". When this happens, the essential oils, herbs or seeds can be added to the soap.

Setting
After pouring into the mould the soap needs to be left to set. Cover with a sheet of cardboard and leave in a warm, dry place. Setting times can vary from soap to soap and depend on a number of factors such as room temperature and ingredients used. As a basic guide, your soap should be solid enough to remove from the mould 24–48 hours after you have poured it. It should be easy enough to cut the soap into bars at this stage.

Curing or maturation
Once the soap has been turned out and cut, it must be allowed to mature for at least four weeks before being used. Any residual sodium hydroxide (lye) is neutralized during this time and sometimes this can result in changes to the appearance of your soap, such as a fine white dust on the surface of the soap (see page 21). Turn the soaps regularly to equalize their drying rates.

EQUIPMENT

GENERAL EQUIPMENT

Most of the equipment you need to make the projects in this book can already be found in your kitchen cupboards. However, it is probably a good idea to keep a few basic utensils, such as a saucepan and some bowls, set aside specially for soapmaking.

Bowls Make sure you have a few measuring bowls to hand for weighing caustic soda and solid oils. Plastic bowls will not be corroded by caustic soda.

Cardboard Sheets of cardboard are used to cover a mould of soap while it sets overnight. You can also use heavy cardboard sheets as cutting boards.

Carving knife You will need a sharp knife to cut your soap into bars. You can use cheese wire but it is often difficult to stop the wire curving. Biscuit cutters can also be used to make novel shapes.

Dark coloured or opaque containers with lids Creams and massage oils are transferred to glass jars or bottles with lids for storage. Dark coloured or opaque jars are particularly useful because they protect the essential oils in the mix from the sun.

Greaseproof paper and scissors You will need to line plastic soap moulds with greaseproof paper, which is simply cut with scissors.

Jam thermometers Jam thermometers are perfect for measuring the temperature of the oils and lye water during soapmaking. It is a good idea to have three thermometers, one for oils, one for lye water and a spare.

Kitchen scales Accurate scales are a necessity when soapmaking. Digital scales are preferable because you will need to measure some ingredients in amounts of less than 5 grams.

Measuring jugs It is useful to have two measuring jugs – one for oil, one for water. Plastic or Pyrex jugs should be used because metal ones will corrode.

Pastry brush Use this to oil the plastic soap mould.

Plastic bucket The bucket you dilute the caustic soda in must be plastic, because metal ones will corrode. A tall bucket is safest since there is less chance of the lye water splashing out.

Plastic moulds You can buy specialist soap moulds, but plastic containers work just as well.

Plastic spatula A plastic spatula will not corrode when used to stir the lye water and the soap mix. You can use a wooden spoon, but it will not last as long.

Spoons Stainless steel spoons can be used to mix the heated oils when making soap. A wooden spoon is used to beat the water and oils together when making creams.

Stainless steel saucepan Use a heavy-bottomed stainless steel saucepan for melting the oils. A double-boiler is not essential for basic soapmaking.

Stainless steel whisk A large stainless steel whisk can be used to whisk creams and mix soap until tracing occurs.

SAFETY EQUIPMENT

The only potentially dangerous processes of soapmaking are handling the caustic soda, the lye water and the raw soap before it has matured, and perhaps using the carving knife to cut it. The following items are necessary for protecting you and your clothes.

Safety first

While soapmaking is relatively easy and fun to do, it does involve caustic substances, high temperatures and chemical reactions, so the following safety considerations should always be followed:

- Wear protective clothing; goggles, a face mask, an apron and long rubber gloves.
- Caustic soda should not be ingested. If it is, go to hospital immediately.
- Always wear goggles when handling caustic material. Splashes on the skin are painful, splashes in your eyes could be devastating. If caustic soda is splashed into the eyes, rinse with cold water and rush to casualty.
- Splashes on the skin at any point during the soapmaking process should be rinsed with vinegar and then water.
- Store caustic soda in an airtight container and label it clearly. Keep it out of the reach of children and pets.
- Do not allow children or pets anywhere near the soapmaking process.
- Keep soapmaking utensils separate from other kitchen utensils.
- Scrape the remains of the soap from the saucepan carefully (wearing rubber gloves) and seal in a bag in the dustbin.
- Carefully wash all the utensils.
- Never leave soap pans unattended. Better to make soap with a friend anyway!

Apron A heavy-duty apron is useful for protecting your clothes from splashes and spills.

Face mask When caustic soda is mixed with water, fumes rise from the bowl, which can be harmful, so wear a mask to stop you breathing them in.

Gloves Protecting your hands is particularly important when handling caustic soda or lye water. At this stage, wear rubber gloves. We wear long ones over a long-sleeved top. Latex gloves are useful when you are cutting and turning the soap, because at this stage you need to be more gentle with it, but remember that it is still caustic until completely cured.

Safety goggles Always wear eye protection during soapmaking and clearing up. Protective goggles can be bought in DIY and hardware stores.

Vinegar Always keep a bottle of vinegar to hand when making soap, because in the event of the caustic mixture spilling or splashing onto your skin, rinsing with vinegar will neutralize the alkali. Rinse off with water..

INGREDIENTS

All the basic ingredients for our recipes are readily available from hardware stores, supermarkets and chemist shops, while wholefood stores are a good place to stock up on herbs. Asian supermarkets will provide coconut oil and palm oil if your normal supermarket does not stock them.

BASE OILS

Many different oils can be used as the base of a soap, massage oil or cream. When soapmaking we tend to combine emollient oils, like olive, coconut, sweet almond and avocado oils, with palm oil, which helps to make a harder soap. As you gain confidence with soapmaking you may want to experiment with other oils and combinations of oils. You may need to vary the amount of lye water you use as different oils have different saponification rates.

Avocado oil High in vitamins A, D and E, avocado oil is excellent for mature, cracked skin. It is revitalizing and healing and regenerates cells.

Beeswax Beeswax is used in the process of making soaps and creams. It can be used in its natural form (yellow beeswax) but bear in mind that this will colour the soap. We use bleached beeswax, which gives the whiteness to our soap recipes. Beeswax thickens other oils to a suitable consistency in creams.

Calendula oil A mildly antiseptic oil that is cleansing, soothing and healing. This oil softens and smoothes skin.

Cocoa butter Cocoa butter attracts and holds moisture to the skin, thus softening it.

Coconut oil This oil comes as a solid and is wonderfully moisturizing. It also makes soap lather.

Evening primrose oil This lovely oil helps prevent premature ageing of the skin.

Olive oil Olive oil prevents loss of natural moisture, as well as softening the skin and attracting external moisture to it.

Palm oil This is another product from the coconut palm and, like coconut oil, it is solid. However, it is slightly creamier and has a softer texture.

Pomace oil This oil is produced from the second and third pressings of the olive. It is slightly cheaper than extra-virgin olive oil.

Rosehip oil A natural preservative, this is sometimes used in shampoos.

Sunflower oil A conditioning oil that stabilizes lather.

Sweet almond oil Sweet almond is a conditioning, emollient oil that softens and smoothes the skin.

Vitamin E oil This is a good oil for preventing wrinkles.

Wheatgerm oil This is good for facial soaps because it is particularly gentle.

THE OTHER ESSENTIALS

The following ingredients form an essential part of the recipes and can be found in large supermarkets or health-food shops.

Caustic soda Otherwise known as sodium hydroxide, this is the alkali that is combined with the acidic oils to make soap. Because it is caustic, the set soap needs to cure for at least four weeks, until the sodium hydroxide is neutralized. Caustic soda can be found in hardware or DIY shops. Make sure the caustic soda you buy is at least 95% pure.

Dead Sea salt This is used to make bath salts and exfoliating scrubs. It is important to use Dead Sea salt, which is purer than any other. Maldon sea salt flakes can also be used as they are slightly less abrasive.

Glycerine This clear, syrupy liquid can be added to soap to increase its moisturizing properties. It is available from pharmacists.

Mineral water Water is a crucial ingredient in soapmaking. Its main job is to dissolve the caustic soda to create lye water. Pure water is best so mineral water or bottled distilled water is a good option.

Vodka We use vodka in some of our recipes – basically because it is the purest form of alcohol. It is a great toner and pore cleanser.

Witch hazel This clear, slightly astringent liquid is available from pharmacists.

ADDITIVES AND EXTRAS

The following ingredients are designed to give your soap or bath product its delicious aroma and wonderful texture and are what makes your homemade spa product such a treat.

Dried flowers and seeds Dried flower petals make a good addition to soaps because they give the soap a pretty, speckled appearance and can have a slightly exfoliating effect. Calendula and chamomile are good examples. We often use mustard seeds as they give soap a wonderful exfoliating action. Dried herbs can also be used in the same way.

Essential oils Essentials oils not only give your homemade bath products the most wonderful scent, they also have properties that affect your health and mood. See pages 16–17 for a glossary of essential oils and their properties. Essential oils can be bought from most chemist shops, and the price of each oil will vary. Essential oils are very potent and only used in small amounts, such as a number of drops. Keep essential oils in a cool, dark place in jars with tight-fitting lids. Use only pure oils.

Seaweed Seaweed is a great product for improving the texture of the skin. You can buy seaweed in powdered form from healthfood stores. We like to use Japanese arame seaweed which has a nice texture and great therapeutic qualities.

GLOSSARY OF ESSENTIAL OILS

Each essential oil has sensual and mood-enhancing properties, and can help to soothe particular ailments.

Bay An uplifting oil ideal for helping to stimulate memory, concentration and confidence. Also good for stomach complaints and aches and pains, and for easing cold and flu symptoms.

Benzoin A beautiful, warm, vanilla-like oil. Its sedative effects make it ideal for dealing with sleep problems, anxiety, grief and real-life crisis. Also excellent for helping relieve asthma, coughs, colds and chills, as well as chilblains.

Bergamot This citrus oil, produced from orange rind, is a refreshing, uplifting oil, good for alleviating anxiety and stress.

Black pepper A stimulating oil that helps strengthen the nerves and mind, as well as warming muscles, making it useful in easing the discomfort of arthritis, muscle pains and sprains.

Cedarwood This is a wonderful tonic to the skin, especially if it is dry or cracked. It can be used to ease coughs, especially the dry persistent type. When used with citrus oils it may lift depression, soothe nerves and ease stress. This deeply relaxing oil is also an aphrodisiac. As popular with men as with women.

Chamomile, Roman A sedative oil ideal for pain of any sort, especially with children. Its soothing qualities help with anxiety, sleep problems and anger, not to mention arthritis, neuralgia, headache, migraine and stomach problems.

Cinnamon Warming and antiseptic, it stimulates and relaxes, giving it a reputation as a mild aphrodisiac.

Clary sage A sedative oil that is ideal for those who find it difficult to switch off. Also excellent for treating pre-menstrual tension and menstrual cramps, as well as muscle pain, labour pain and night sweats. It is also a good skin conditioner.

Eucalyptus An oil to revive the spirit and ease cough and cold symptoms, muscular pain and arthritis. Eucalyptus boosts immunity and can ease headaches, sinusitis and insect bites, as well as repelling insects.

Frankincense A sedative oil ideal for addressing sleep problems and anxiety, helping produce feelings of inner peace and acceptance. Useful in treating coughs and asthma, and a great addition to face creams for dry or mature skin.

Geranium An uplifting oil ideal for helping ease mood swings, post-natal depression and pre-menstrual tension. It is used a lot in beauty care because it is good for most skin types. It is also an excellent mosquito repellent.

Ginger A stimulating, warm oil ideal for treating muscle pain and arthritic joint problems, sprains and strains. It eases coughs and colds and boosts immunity, as well as easing stomach problems like sickness, travel sickness and nausea.

Grapefruit A refreshing and reviving oil with euphoric qualities. It is great to use for oily or congested skin. Excellent for use with depression and exhaustion.

Juniper berry This oil is known for its detoxification properties, which is why it is used to treat arthritis, hangovers, water retention, cellulite and to clear emotional "baggage" that stops you from moving on in life. Invaluable!

Lavender What can't this oil do? It can be used neat to ease burns, scalds, sunburn, arthritis and any "hot" conditions, because of its cooling effects. It can help alleviate eczema, acne, insect bites, stings, head lice, bruises, headaches, vertigo, migraine, fainting, aches, pains and sprains.

Lemon Ideal for treating cold sores, verrucas, warts, athlete's foot and spots. A very uplifting detox oil that is used for cellulite, gout, arthritis, colds, flu, infection and for helping reduce nightmares when mixed with a suitable sedative oil, especially with children.

Lemongrass An uplifting, refreshing oil that can be used to treat excessive perspiration, athlete's foot, muscle pain, poor circulation, head lice and help improve muscle tone.

Lime An uplifting member of the citrus oil family with a mouth-watering aroma.

Mandarin An uplifting oil that smells good enough to eat, so no surprise that it is used to treat stomach problems and depression. Children love it and an anxious child responds well to having it rubbed clockwise into the tummy (in dilution of course). Also used to reduce stretch marks and scarring, reduce pre-menstrual tension and increase appetite, especially following illness.

May chang This uplifting oil is great for helping ease depression and keep away the winter blues.

Myrrh Myrrh is a deep smelling oil with a warm, woody aroma, useful for dealing with sorrow, anger, rejection and promoting feelings of tranquillity. It is also excellent for treating athlete's foot and other fungal infections, not to mention asthma, coughs, gum infections, thrush and to boost immunity. A very powerful antiseptic.

Patchouli An excellent tonic for the skin, patchouli can be used to treat athlete's foot, acne, dandruff and eczema. It is also an insect repellent, and has been used as an aphrodisiac. It can ease depression, and, in small doses, lethargy.

Peppermint This stimulating oil can be used to ease headaches and migraines if used at the onset of an attack. It can aid memory and ease fatigue. It also warms muscles and eases pains, colds, coughs and flu. It can also help ease colic and stomach cramps, as well as fainting.

Petitgrain This oil is widely used for combating the winter blues (SAD). It is ideal for convalescence, nervous exhaustion, mild depression, nervous debility and self-blame. It is also used to treat acne and oily skin.

Rosemary This is as useful as lavender in that it can treat dandruff, lice, varicose veins and scabies, as well as muscle pains, arthritis, rheumatism, cellulite, poor circulation, digestion problems, bronchitis, whooping cough, coughs, colds, flu, debility, headaches, poor memory, neuralgia and more.

Sage Used in very small amounts, this oil is soothing and antiseptic, excellent for joints and muscles. Reduces sweatiness.

Sweet orange An uplifting oil that is good for tension and depression – good for people who find it hard to switch off.

Tangerine A light, happy citrus oil with uplifting, freshening properties.

Tea tree Well known for its antiseptic, antiviral and antibacterial properties, tea tree is also good for combating fungal infections, catarrh, sinusitis, chest infections, mouth ulcers, verrucas, athlete's foot, spots, boils, insect bites, cystitis and thrush. It is good for convalescence, even after shock.

Thyme Excellent to burn if there is an epidemic around. It can treat colds, coughs and flu and ease headaches, pain, sciatica and sprains.

Ylang ylang This floral, exotic oil has been used widely to ease stress, depression, fear, anger, (especially if it is born of frustration) high blood pressure, shock, panic attacks and palpitations. It is also useful for general skin care and is an aphrodisiac to boot. Lovely mixed with citrus oils to make it lighter and more refreshing.

Safety with essential oils

Essential oils are concentrated and, although beneficial, their strength and effect should not be underestimated. In this book we have suggested essential oils to be used in the recipes. These will suit most people, but if you have a particular health problem, are on medication or are pregnant, you should seek professional medical advice before using any essential oils. Some essential oils can be harmful if used inappropriately.

- Do not use undiluted essential oils directly on the skin – except lavender which can be used in very small doses.
- Do not ingest the oils.
- Avoid contact with the eyes.
- If you have sensitive skin or allergies consult a professional before using essential oils.
- Keep essential oils out of the reach of children.
- Avoid using citrus oils (bergamot, grapefruit, lemon, lime, mandarin, sweet orange, tangerine) for at least 12 hours before sunbathing or using a sunbed.

THE BASIC TECHNIQUES

Each of the recipes in this book has a full set of instructions. However, you may find it useful to look at the following photographs and step-by-step instructions before you begin a recipe, to ensure that you are confident with the whole technique.

SOAPMAKING: THE COLD PROCESS METHOD

This book uses the cold process method of making soap, which is the most natural and does not involve the use of chemical additives. Commercial soap is often made using tallow (animal fat) and contains many synthetic perfumes, colours and preservatives. For this reason it can dry and irritate the skin, in fact many people believe they are sensitive to all soaps, when in fact they would be perfectly all right using our gentle, natural, therapeutic bars. Follow our simple soapmaking instructions and experience the difference.

1 Use a pastry brush and a little sunflower oil to lightly grease a plastic mould. You can buy custom-made soap moulds but plastic food storage containers and trays work just as well. Line the base and sides of the mould with greaseproof paper, tidying the corners and smoothing down well. Use more oil to "stick down" any loose bits of paper.

2 Measure the solid oils first and place them in a heavy-based stainless steel saucepan. Measure the liquid oils and add these to the pan.

3 Heat the oils over a gentle heat, stirring with a stainless steel spoon or plastic spatula until the oils are combined.

Think ahead
Making soap is a bit like cooking – some people find it daunting at first. As with cooking, it is best to have all your ingredients and equipment ready at the start. Make sure that the base oils, lye water ingredients, essential oils, herbs, seeds and petals are measured and ready to hand, so that you don't find yourself searching for an ingredient at a crucial moment and ruining the process.

4 Make sure the room is well ventilated and wear goggles, a face mask, rubber gloves and an apron. Weigh the caustic soda in a plastic bowl and set aside. Pour a measured amount of mineral water into a plastic bucket. Carefully pour the caustic soda into the mineral water. Fumes will be given off at this stage. Stir with a plastic spatula until dissolved. The caustic mixture (lye water) will be very hot at this point.

5 Use a jam thermometer to test the temperature of the lye water as it cools. To help cool it, place the bucket in a sink of cold water and stir. When it nears the required temperature, reheat or cool the base oils as required. Both the lye water and the melted oils need to reach the same temperature of 55°C (131°F), and you will need two thermometers to monitor this.

6 When both the oils and the lye water have reached the right temperature, remove the pan from the heat and pour the lye water into the oils. Stir thoroughly with a whisk and continue until tracing occurs. This is when the soap thickens and a spoonful of soap drizzled over the surface leaves a visible line. It can take 10 minutes or an hour, depending on the oils used. The soaps in this book will all trace within 20 minutes.

7 Add the essential oils, herbs, petals or seeds at this stage, stirring thoroughly.

8 Pour the mixture into the prepared mould. Place in a safe, warm and dry place. Cover the mould with cardboard and leave for 24 hours.

9 Wearing protective gloves, turn out the soap onto greaseproof paper. Use a carving knife to cut the soap into bars and lay them out on a tray covered with greaseproof paper, with room for air to circulate around them. Place in a warm, dry place to cure. Leave for four weeks, turning occasionally to dry all sides.

Alternatively, use biscuit cutters to make shaped soaps. Simply press the cutter firmly and evenly into the soap after you have turned it out, and leave to cure as above.

MAKING HERBAL INFUSIONS

Herbal infusions are used in a number of recipes in this book but they are also a great way to tone your skin, as well as being inexpensive. Simply infuse flowers, such as calendula (pot marigold), lime, elder or chamomile to make a very effective face splash, although it will only keep for a few days, so use it liberally. It can be mixed with witch hazel in equal parts for a slightly astringent toner that is ideal for normal, combination or oily skin.

1 Place a double handful of flowers in a jug and pour over 600 ml (1 pint) of boiling water – although this is not an exact science. Cover and leave to cool.

2 Strain the mixture and keep it in the fridge. It is incredibly refreshing and great for hair too, if you really strain all the bits out.

MAKING SKIN CREAMS

There is no caustic material used in the making of creams, so no particular safety tips are applicable. Just take care as you would with cooking – wear an apron to protect clothes and handle hot fats and water carefully. Our creams do not contain preservatives, so should be made in small quantities and used within a month. Keep them refrigerated where possible or in a cool dark place.

1 Measure the oils and place in a stainless steel saucepan. Set over a low heat and stir gently until all the oils have melted.

2 Measure the water and add to the oils in the pan, whisking or stirring with a wooden spoon until the mixture thickens and turns creamy.

3 Remove from the heat and stir until the cream has cooled to room temperature. Add the essential oils.

4 Transfer to glass jars with lids and shake gently until the cream has cooled, to stop the oil and water separating.

MAKING OILS

Simple recipes such as the Wide Awake Massage Oil on page 26 or the Thymeless Sleep Oil on page 78 do not require any complicated techniques. Simply measure the oils as directed and pour into a suitable container with a tight-fitting lid. Shake gently to mix.

MAKING SALTS AND SCRUBS

Salts and scrubs are straightforward to make, and no caustic material is used. The salts should be used within two months.

1 Mix all the oils together, then stir in the Dead Sea salt.

2 Transfer the salts to a dark glass jar with a lid.

TROUBLESHOOTING

Don't worry, we all have the odd disaster from time to time. Some can be overcome, while others may mean that you have to start all over again.

RELATIVELY MINOR PROBLEMS

These errors may result in a soap that is not as visually appealing as it should be, but on that can still be used.

Soft soap If the soap is too soft to cut, you may have used too little caustic soda, or it was not pure (it should be 95% at least). Leave a little longer to dry then try to cut it again, it may dry after a few more weeks.

Crumbly soap This soap has lost heat too rapidly, or may have been combined at too low a temperature. It can be used but may not look as good as usual. Test the pH to be on the safe side.

White film A white film on the surface of the soap is nothing to worry about, just a little soda ash. Scrape it off to make the soap look more attractive.

Oil on the surface A little oil on the surface means that the soap may have been stirred too little. The oil may sink with time, otherwise it can be wiped off when the soap is cut. Test for pH, because if too much oil is lost the soap will be caustic.

No tracing Certain oils take longer to saponify, such as extra-virgin olive oil, so just keep stirring. If after one hour there is still no tracing it may be due to the lye being poured into the oils at too low a temperature. Time to start again, I'm afraid.

Seizing Occasionally the soap will suddenly thicken on the addition of certain essential oils, notably clove. This can be alarming but don't worry, just pour it immediately into the mould. If the surface won't flatten make a nice pattern with a fork and knife, like icing a cake.

BIG TROUBLE: DISCARD THE SOAP

I'm afraid there is no hope if your soap has any of these problems. Don't even think about using it.

Air pockets filled with liquid This problem is due to insufficient stirring, but, more importantly, the soap may be caustic and should not be used.

Thick layer of oil on the surface This problem is usually due to lack of stirring or a rapid temperature loss. If too much oil separates then the soap will be too caustic and must be discarded.

Large amounts of white powder This is caused by too much caustic soda in the mix. It also means that the pH balance of the soap is too high so the soap must be discarded.

Brittle soap Again, this occurs when there is too much caustic soda in the soap and means the soap will have to be discarded.

REFRESH & REVIVE

SUNNY SOAP

Ingredients

310 ml (11 fl oz) mineral water

A handful each of lavatera and chamomile flowers

225 ml (8 fl oz) sunflower oil

225 ml (8 fl oz) pomace or olive oil

200 g (7 oz) coconut oil

100 g (4 oz) caustic soda

10 ml (2 tsp) bergamot essential oil

6 ml (1 tsp) sweet orange essential oil

6 ml (1 tsp) ylang ylang essential oil

3 ml ($^{1}/_{2}$ tsp) tangerine essential oil

Equipment

General equipment (see page 12)

Safety equipment (see page 13)

Sieve

Wooden board

Tray

Method

1 Work in a well-ventilated room. Oil and line a plastic mould with greaseproof paper.

2 Prepare the mineral water by boiling and infusing the chamomile and lavatera flowers (see page 20). Allow to cool completely then strain and reserve the infusion and the flowers.

3 Melt the sunflower, pomace and coconut oils in a large stainless steel saucepan over a low heat.

4 Wearing protective goggles, a mask, an apron and long rubber gloves, add the caustic soda to the infused mineral water in a plastic bucket. Stir with a plastic spatula until dissolved.

5 Using one jam thermometer for the oils and another for the caustic soda mixture (lye water), monitor both solutions until they reach 35.5°C (96°F). Still wearing the protective clothing, immediately pour the lye water into the oils. Continuously stir for approximately 15 minutes with the spatula and you will see the mixture thickening.

6 Tracing occurs when a drizzle of the mixture on the surface of the soap leaves a visible line. At this point pour in the essential oils and combine thoroughly. Add half of the chamomile and lavatera flowers to give texture and mix until evenly distributed.

7 Pour the soap mixture into the prepared mould and place in a safe, warm, dry place for 24 hours, covering with cardboard to keep the heat in.

8 Wearing protective gloves – the soap is still caustic at this point – turn the soap out onto a wooden board covered with greaseproof paper. Peel off the lining paper and cut the bar into the desired shapes using a carving knife or biscuit cutters. If the mixture is too soft to cut, leave for a further 24 hours. Space out the cut soaps on greaseproof paper in a tray and leave in a dark, warm, dry place for four weeks to mature, turning several times.

This easy-to-make soap has a base of **sunflower** oil and pomace oil. Pomace oil is the last pressing of olive oil and speeds up the tracing time of the soap. However, if you can't find it in the supermarket you can use normal olive oil instead. **Coconut oil** is added for lather and its moisturizing properties. A blend of citrus essential oils contains bergamot, which is **stimulating** to those early morning senses, and sweet orange oil for a real sunshine feeling and aroma. Sensual **ylang ylang** will leave you feeling fresh and in a good mood all day.

The **zingy**, zesty combination of grapefruit and mandarin essential oils will really **wake you up** in the morning and leave a wonderful fresh aroma on the skin.

Lavender and mandarin are excellent **essential oils** for **sensitive** skins and this delicious oil also has useful insect repellent properties for the summer months and holidays abroad.

WIDE AWAKE MASSAGE OIL

Ingredients
250 ml (9 fl oz) sweet almond oil

5 drops grapefruit essential oil

10 drops mandarin essential oil

2 drops lavender essential oil

Equipment
Dark or clear glass bottle with tight-fitting lid

Method

1 Pour all the ingredients into a dark or clear glass bottle and shake gently to mix. A clear glass bottle should be stored in a dark place to protect the essential oils from the light.

2 Rub the oil into the skin in the morning and imagine you are waking up to the scent of lavender fields wafting on a gentle Mediterranean breeze and looking out over orchards of almonds and oranges.

Safety consideration
If you have a serious nut allergy you will need to replace the sweet almond oil. Grapeseed and sunflower oils make good alternatives.

Do not use citrus essential oils if you are likely to be exposed to the sun, since it makes the skin more sensitive to sunlight.

MORNING GLORY SOAP

Ingredients

200 ml (7 fl oz) pomace or olive oil

100 ml (4 fl oz) sweet almond oil

75 ml (3 fl oz) sunflower oil

65 g (2½ oz) coconut oil

60 g (2½ oz) palm oil

25 ml (1 fl oz) calendula oil

40 g (1½ oz) beeswax

65 g (2½ oz) caustic soda

230 ml (8 fl oz) mineral water

7 ml (1 tsp) lime essential oil

5 ml (1 tsp) sweet orange essential oil

5 ml (1 tsp) may chang essential oil

2 ml (½ tsp) frankincense essential oil

Petals from 20 dried calendula flowers

Equipment

General equipment (see page 12)

Safety equipment (see page 13)

Wooden board

Tray

Method

1 Work in a well-ventilated room. Oil and line a plastic mould with greaseproof paper.

2 Melt the pomace, sweet almond, sunflower, coconut, palm and calendula oils with the beeswax in a large stainless steel saucepan over a low heat.

3 Wearing protective goggles, a mask, an apron and long rubber gloves, pour the caustic soda into the mineral water in a plastic bucket and stir with a plastic spatula to dissolve.

4 Using one jam thermometer for the oils and one for the caustic soda mixture (lye water), monitor each mix until they both reach 55°C (131°F).

5 Still wearing the protective clothing, immediately pour the lye water into the oils. Continuously stir with the spatula for approximately 15 minutes and you will see the mixture thickening.

6 Tracing occurs when a drizzle of the mixture on the surface of the soap leaves a visible line. At this point, pour in the essential oils and mix well. Add the calendula petals and stir until evenly distributed.

7 Pour the soap into the prepared mould. At this stage the soap is thick enough to have a pattern made across its surface. Drag a fork across the top to make a ripple pattern, first one way and then the other, or design your own motif.

8 Leave to set in a warm, dry place, covered with cardboard to keep the heat in. After 24 hours, turn it out onto a wooden board covered with greaseproof paper. The soap is still caustic at this stage so wear gloves to peel off the soap's lining paper and use a carving knife to cut it into chunky bars of approximately 100 g (4 oz). Set out the soaps on a tray lined with greaseproof paper and leave to mature for four weeks in a dry, warm place, turning occasionally.

Use this soap first thing and you'll be ready to take on the world. It is a **deliciously indulgent** blend of skin conditioning essential oils. What's more, there's no need to moisturize after using this one. Calendula oil and **sweet orange** essential oil are known for their healing properties and will leave your skin feeling silky soft throughout the day. Frankincense has been used for centuries as an antiseptic with powers to neutralize offensive odours, while lime and may chang are **reviving** oils and will add an exotic touch to your morning shower.

Most skins will benefit from this healthy mixture of avocado oil and **sweet almond oil**. We have added lemon and geranium essential oils, not just for their benefits in **revitalizing** and **refreshing** the skin, but for their wonderfully uplifting aroma. If you are a sun worshipper replace the lemon oil with lavender (see note about **citrus oils** on page 17).

MEGA MOISTURIZING CREAM

Ingredients

40 ml (1¹/₂ fl oz) sweet almond oil

20 ml (1 fl oz) avocado oil

15 g (¹/₂ oz) beeswax

30 ml (2 tbsp) mineral water

2 drops lemon essential oil

1 drop geranium essential oil

Equipment

Stainless steel saucepan

Wooden spoon

Dark or clear glass jar with lids

Method

1 Melt the oils together in a heavy-bottomed stainless steel pan. Warm the water and beat it slowly into the oils.

2 Remove from the heat and stir until the cream cools to blood temperature. Stir in the essential oils and combine thoroughly to make a smooth cream.

3 Spoon into glass jars and shake until the lotion has cooled completely, to stop the oil and water phases separating while warm. Store clear glass jars in a dark place to protect the essential oils from the light.

KEEN AS MUSTARD SOAP

Ingredients

200 ml (7 fl oz) extra-virgin olive oil

100 ml (4 fl oz) sunflower oil

65 g (2^1/$_2$ oz) palm oil

60 g (2^1/$_2$ oz) coconut oil

25 ml (1 fl oz) sweet almond oil

40 g (1^1/$_2$ oz) beeswax

65 g (2^1/$_2$ oz) caustic soda

230 ml (8 fl oz) mineral water

10 ml (2 tsp) lemongrass essential oil

6 ml (1 tsp) lime essential oil

2 ml (^{1}/$_2$ tsp) rosemary essential oil

2 drops benzoin essential oil

2 tbsp mustard seeds

Equipment

General equipment (see page 12)

Safety equipment (see page 13)

Wooden board

Tray

Method

1. Work in a well-ventilated area. Oil and line a plastic mould with greaseproof paper.

2. Melt the olive, sunflower, palm, coconut and sweet almond oils with the beeswax in a large stainless steel saucepan over a low heat.

3. Wearing protective goggles, a mask, an apron and long rubber gloves, pour the caustic soda into the mineral water in a plastic bucket. Stir with a plastic spatula until dissolved.

4. Using one jam thermometer for the oils and another for the caustic soda mixture (lye water), let both solutions reach 55°C (131°F). At this point, wearing the protective clothing, pour the lye water into the oils and combine thoroughly with the spatula.

5. Keep stirring until tracing occurs – when a drizzle of the mixture on the surface of the soap leaves a visible line. Add the essential oils and then the mustard seeds, mixing well.

6. Pour into the prepared mould and leave for 24 hours, covered with cardboard, in a dry, warm place.

7. Wearing rubber gloves, turn out the soap onto a wooden board covered with greaseproof paper. Cut into bars with a carving knife and space out on a tray lined with greaseproof paper in a warm dark place for four weeks, turning regularly.

8. Use before a busy day or a night out, to give you extra energy.

> **A holiday favourite**
> Lemongrass and lime essential oils are both insect repellants so this is a great soap to use during the summer or to take on holiday.

Fabulous in the shower and with an aroma loved equally by men and women, this soap is a sizzling mixture of lime and lemongrass essential oils to freshen the body, and rosemary to revive the senses. Lemongrass has a stimulating effect on the whole system and has antiseptic and deodorizing properties, and rosemary is a real wake-up oil. Used for many centuries in medicines, rosemary will revive your senses, both physical and mental. The joy of this soap is the real mustard seeds, which will smooth all the rough edges with a gentle exfoliating action.

For many men, the days of a leisurely shave with brush and bowl are gone. Instead, shaving is part of their shower routine. So, we have come up with this **delectably** moisturizing soap that combines the emollient properties of avocado oil with the freshness of cedarwood and clary sage essential oils, with their **nutty aromas** and skin conditioning properties. Both essential oils have **aphrodisiac** properties and will give you a sexy, masculine feeling to start the day.

SMOOTHING SHAVE SOAP

Ingredients
250 ml (9 fl oz) olive oil

75 ml (3 fl oz) avocado oil

60 g (2¹/₂ oz) coconut oil

40 g (1¹/₂ oz) palm oil

40 g (1¹/₂ oz) beeswax

25 g (1 oz) cocoa butter

65 g (2¹/₂ oz) caustic soda

230 ml (8 fl oz) mineral water

13 ml (3 tsp) clary sage essential oil

6 ml (1 tsp) cedarwood essential oil

Equipment
General equipment (see page 12)

Safety equipment (see page 13)

Wooden board

Tray

Method

1 Work in a well-ventilated room. Oil a plastic mould and line with greaseproof paper.

2 Melt the olive, avocado, coconut and palm oils with the beeswax and cocoa butter in a large stainless steel saucepan over a low heat.

3 Wearing protective eyewear, a mask, an apron and long rubber gloves, pour the mineral water into a plastic bucket and slowly pour in the caustic soda, stirring to dissolve using a plastic spatula.

4 Use one jam thermometer for the caustic soda mix (lye water) and one for the oil mixture. Monitor both mixtures until they equalize at 55°C (131°F). Wearing the protective clothing, immediately pour the lye water into the oils, stirring continuously with the spatula until well combined.

5 Continue stirring until tracing occurs (see page 11) and then pour in the essential oils and stir in thoroughly. Pour the mixture into the prepared mould and swirl the surface with the spatula if you are going to cut the soap into bars, or leave it smooth.

6 Leave to set in a warm, dry place for 24 hours, covered with cardboard to keep the heat in. Wearing protective gloves, turn the soap out onto a wooden board lined with greaseproof paper, and cut into bars or rounds with a carving knife or biscuit cutter. Set out the soaps on a tray lined with greaseproof paper and leave in a warm, dry place for four weeks to mature, turning occasionally.

> **One for the shaving bowl**
> If you use a shaving bowl, simply make the soap up as normal, then, when it is set, use a round cutter that is just smaller in diameter than the bowl.

Black pepper, as you would expect, has a **powerful** stimulant effect, a property that is put to very good use in this pre-sport rub. Combined with **rosemary**, the wake-up herb, these essential oils will also sharpen your concentration and help your joints and muscles cope with the demands of exercise, minimizing pain and stiffness afterwards. As this is designed to improve **performance** and prevent fatigue, no sportsman or sportswoman can afford to leave home without this magical cream.

SPRINT PRE-EXERCISE MASSAGE CREAM

Ingredients

50 g (2 oz) coconut oil

30 ml (1 fl oz) sweet almond oil

15 g (1/2 oz) beeswax

15 g (1/2 oz) cocoa butter

60 ml (2 1/2 fl oz) mineral water

7 ml (1 1/2 tsp) rosemary essential oil

3 ml (1/2 tsp) black pepper essential oil

Equipment

Stainless steel saucepan

Wooden spoon

Dark or clear glass jars with lids

Method

1 Place the coconut and sweet almond oils in a heavy-bottomed stainless steel saucepan with the beeswax and cocoa butter. Gently melt them over a low heat. Beat in the mineral water with a wooden spoon until a smooth cream is obtained.

2 Remove from the heat and keep stirring until the cream has cooled to blood temperature. Stir in the essential oils.

3 Spoon into glass jars and shake until the lotion has cooled completely, to stop the oil and water phases of the cream separating while warm. Store clear jars in a dark place to preserve the oils.

4 Your mind and body will be ready for any kind of action after rubbing this one on!

Aah, **peppermint**! If ever there was an essential oil to put a spring in your step, this is the one. Peppermint, with its **cooling**, refreshing and **energizing** properties, will stimulate your mind and body, wake you up and prepare your feet for the rigours of the day. A little thyme essential oil has been added as an antiseptic and because it is good at **fighting fatigue**. This cream is definitely not one to use at bedtime.

COOL AND MINTY FOOT CREAM

Ingredients

50 g (2 oz) coconut oil

30 ml (1 fl oz) calendula oil

15 g (1/2 oz) beeswax

15 g (1/2 oz) cocoa butter

60 ml (2 1/2 fl oz) mineral water

8 ml (1 1/2 tsp) peppermint essential oil

2 ml (1/2 tsp) thyme essential oil

Equipment

Stainless steel saucepan

Wooden spoon

Dark or clear glass jars with lids

Method

1 Place the coconut and calendula oils in a heavy-bottomed stainless steel saucepan with the beeswax and cocoa butter. Gently melt them over a low heat. Beat in the mineral water with a wooden spoon.

2 Remove from the heat and stir until the cream cools to blood temperature. Stir in the essential oils, making sure that they are thoroughly combined to make a smooth cream.

3 Spoon into glass jars and shake until the lotion has cooled completely, to stop the oil and water phases separating while warm. Store clear glass jars in a dark place to protect the essential oils from the light.

4 Rub into the feet first thing in the morning or in preparation for a night out dancing. If you love the aroma as much as we do, you can actually use it all over and it will leave the skin feeling cool and refreshed.

HAIR BARE SHAMPOO BAR

Ingredients

700 ml (1 pint) olive oil

90 ml (3½ fl oz) sweet almond oil

60 g (2½ oz) beeswax

55 g (2 oz) creamed coconut

270 ml (9 fl oz) mineral water

Six handfuls of nettle tops

113 g (4½ oz) caustic soda

22 ml (1 fl oz) bergamot essential oil

8 ml (1½ tsp) lavender essential oil

8 ml (1½ tsp) lemongrass essential oil

Equipment

General equipment (see page 12)

Safety equipment (see page 13)

Sieve

Wooden board

Tray

Method

1 Work in a well-ventilated room. Oil and line a plastic mould with greaseproof paper.

2 Prepare the mineral water by boiling and infusing the nettle tops (see page 20). Allow to cool completely, then strain and reserve the infusion. Chop the infused nettles finely and set aside.

3 Melt the olive and sweet almond oils with the beeswax and creamed coconut in a large stainless steel saucepan over a low heat. Stir well using a stainless steel spoon, and do not allow the coconut cream to "catch" on the bottom.

4 Wearing protective goggles, a mask, an apron and long rubber gloves, add the caustic soda to the infused mineral water in a plastic bucket. Stir with a plastic spatula until dissolved.

5 Using one jam thermometer for the oils and another for the caustic soda mixture (lye water), allow both solutions to reach 55°C (131°F). At this point, still wearing the protective clothing, pour the lye water into the oil mixture, stirring continuously with the spatula.

6 Keep stirring until the solution traces – when a drizzle of mixture leaves a line on the surface of the soap. Pour in the essential oils, thoroughly incorporating them into the soap. Add the chopped nettles and stir.

7 Pour the soap into the prepared mould, cover with cardboard and leave in a safe, warm, dry place for 24 hours.

8 Wearing protective gloves, turn the soap out onto a wooden board covered with greaseproof paper. Peel off the lining paper and cut the soap into the desired shape using a carving knife or biscuit cutters. Space the cut soaps out on a tray lined with greaseproof paper and leave to mature for four weeks in a dry, dark place, turning several times.

Hair rinsed in an infusion of nettles will be **shiny** and well conditioned, a property we have utilized in this shampoo bar. The basis of this soap is an infusion of young nettle tips in mineral water. This is combined with **bergamot**, lavender and lemongrass essential oils to stimulate the scalp and prevent dandruff and flakiness of the scalp, as well as imparting a **delightful** citrus aroma.

More and more men are overcoming their fears when it comes to using **moisturizers**. The combination of bay, cedarwood and clary sage essential oils in this moisturizer, designed specifically for men, is a classic and leaves a lingering but not too overpowering aroma on the skin. Bay has great **healing** and antiseptic properties, to soothe skin irritated after shaving, and a spicy, masculine fragrance, ideal for men's toiletries. A herbal infusion is included and can be varied according to skin type. Chamomile is useful for irritated, inflamed skin; calendula flowers for combination skin; elderflowers for sallow skin; and lemon balm leaves or lime flowers for **all skin types**.

BAYWATCH FACE CREAM FOR MEN

Ingredients

A handful of dried flowers such as chamomile, calendula or elderflower

20 g (^{3}/$_4$ oz) beeswax

20 ml (1 fl oz) rosehip oil

40 ml (1^1/$_2$ fl oz) sweet almond oil

10 drops clary sage essential oil

4 drops cedarwood essential oil

2 drops bay essential oil

Equipment

Measuring jug

Sieve

Stainless steel saucepan

Wooden spoon

Dark or clear glass jars with lids

Method

1 Make a herbal infusion with the dried flowers and 300 ml (10 fl oz) boiling water (see page 20). Strain and set aside to cool.

2 Melt the beeswax in a heavy-bottomed stainless steel saucepan, then add the rosehip and sweet almond oils, beating steadily with a wooden spoon. Add 40 ml (1^1/$_2$ fl oz) of the herbal infusion in a slow trickle.

3 Take the saucepan off the heat and continue to stir until the lotion has cooled to blood temperature. Stir in the essential oils.

4 Decant the cream into glass jars and place the lids on tightly. Now shake the mixture until the lotion has entirely cooled – this process will prevent the oil and water phases of the lotion separating while the cream is still warm. Store clear glass jars in a dark place to preserve the essential oils.

5 Use in the morning or before bed to give your face some love and attention.

There are many and varied brands of aftershave on the market, but if you want to really **look after your skin** it is nice to know exactly what goes into the product, or, even better, to make your own. The essential oils in this aftershave splash have been chosen for their **therapeutic** values and lasting, but not overpowering, aromas. You can use them as suggested or **mix** them to your own preference, within the suggested quantities.

CLOSE SHAVE AFTERSHAVE SPLASH

Ingredients

25 ml (1 fl oz) vodka

250 ml (9 fl oz) witch hazel

3 drops bay essential oil

3 drops lime essential oil or 25 ml (1 fl oz) vodka

3 drops bergamot essential oil

3 drops cedarwood essential oil

Equipment

Dark or clear glass bottle with tight-fitting lid

Method

1 Mix together all the ingredients in a dark or clear glass bottle with a lid. If using a clear glass bottle remember to store the mix in a dark place to ensure the essential oils are well preserved.

2 Shake the mixture well before use, then simply pour a little into the hand and splash away.

Therapeutic benefits

Bay essential oil is antiseptic and bactericidal, while lime has a cooling, refreshing aroma and uplifts the spirits. The essential oil of bergamot is a mood-enhancer so is guaranteed to leave you with a spring in your step and a smile on your face. Cedarwood's use in skin preparations for men reflects its antiseptic and astringent properties and its masculine aroma (with a reputation as an aphrodisiac too).

Witch hazel is a tonic and astringent as well as a sedative, and so wonderfully soothing. Vodka gives the great cool, tingly feeling that every good aftershave should give, and the cheapest brand will do.

Safety consideration

Citrus essential oils make the skin more sensitive to sunlight, so do not use them if you are likely to be exposed to the sun.

GIFTWRAPPING IDEAS

These soaps and other bathroom gifts look wonderful when wrapped in brightly coloured ribbons.

Why not package up one of the soaps with a soft face cloth to make a really special gift? Tissue

paper, cellophane and sheer fabric are all pretty ways of wrapping items. Corrugated cardboard

not only protects glass bottles but it makes an alternative wrapping, especially when decorated

with a slice of dried fruit.

PAMPER & INDULGE

Summer time is exposure time for feet, which could be embarrassing if yours have hard skin, cracked heels, discoloured nails . . . need I go on? In this case drastic measures are needed, so we have pulled out all the stops. Tried and tested on the most horrible of feet, not only the look but also the smell will be transformed with this foot scrub.

WELL-HEELED FOOT SCRUB

Ingredients

100 ml (4 fl oz) sweet almond oil

8 drops lemon essential oil

4 drops tea tree essential oil

2 drops myrrh essential oil

200 g (7 oz) Maldon salt flakes

Equipment

Mixing bowl

Spoon

Dark or clear glass jars with lids

Method

1 Mix together the sweet almond oil and essential oils, then add the salt and stir well. Keep in dark jars or store the scrub in clear glass jars in a dark place, to ensure that the aroma is preserved.

2 Before using the scrub, wash your feet and soak them in warm water for about five minutes, to soften the skin. Dry the feet, then scoop out a handful of scrub and, keeping the foot over a bowl or bath to avoid making a mess, massage all over the foot, paying particular attention to areas of hard skin. Rinse the salt off with tepid water, then pat dry with a soft towel. Your feet will never have felt so good. Put on a pair of cotton socks that will allow the oils to sink in and do their job, without making greasy, slippery footprints.

A treat for feet

Lemon essential oil is enormously beneficial for feet. Having a mild bleaching action to revive skin, it aids brittle nails, treats verrucas and corns, stimulates the circulation and helps to rid the body of acidity – in cases of gout, for instance. Tea tree is a powerful antiseptic and, when blended with lemon essential oil, the aroma is one of those magical combinations. A couple of drops of myrrh essential oil make a useful addition to this scrub because myrrh is antifungal, particularly useful to feet in hot weather.

Safety consideration

Do not use myrrh essential oil while pregnant. For this recipe simply remove the myrrh.

BAYSIC INSTINCT SOAP FOR MEN

Ingredients

A handful of bay leaves

225 ml (8 fl oz) sunflower oil

225 ml (8 fl oz) olive oil

200 g (7 oz) coconut oil

100 g (4 oz) caustic soda

310 ml (11 fl oz) mineral water

*11 ml (2 tsp) bergamot
essential oil*

8 ml (1½ tsp) bay essential oil

5 ml (1 tsp) patchouli essential oil

*3 ml (½ tsp) cinnamon
essential oil*

Equipment

General equipment (see page 12)

Safety equipment (see page 13)

Wooden board

Tray

Method

1 Work in a well-ventilated area. Oil and line a plastic mould with greaseproof paper.

2 If you don't have a bay tree in the garden, bay leaves are readily available fresh or dried at the supermarket. Chop a handful of leaves very small, removing and discarding the veins.

3 Melt the sunflower, olive and coconut oils together in a large stainless steel saucepan over a low heat.

4 Wearing protective goggles, a face mask, an apron and long rubber gloves, add the caustic soda to the mineral water in a plastic bucket and stir well with a plastic spatula until thoroughly dissolved.

5 Using one jam thermometer for the oils and another for the caustic soda mixture (lye water), allow both solutions to reach 35.5°C (96°F). Still wearing the protective clothing, immediately pour the lye water into the oils and stir thoroughly. Continue stirring with the spatula until the mixture traces – when a drizzle of the mix leaves a visible line on the surface of the soap.

6 Now add the essential oils and chopped bay leaves, mixing them evenly into the soap.

7 Pour the soap into the prepared mould, cover with cardboard to keep the heat in, and leave in a warm, dry, safe, place for 24 hours.

8 Wearing protective gloves, turn out the soap onto a wooden board covered with greaseproof paper. Peel off the lining paper and cut into chunky bars using a carving knife. Lay the soaps on a tray covered with greaseproof paper, spacing them to allow for air circulation. Store in a dark, dry, warm place for four weeks, turning several times during the maturing process.

This soap is dedicated to Eva French, a **wonderful** Jamaican lady from New York, who so impressed Ada with her relaxed Caribbean style that she created this soap in her honour. The rich, **warm aroma** of bay leaves is the essence of Bay Rum, the traditional cologne of the West Indies. In Ancient Greece, sporting champions were crowned with bay leaves – what better scent, then, could there be to give a heroic husband or boyfriend. Combining fresh bay leaves with bay, bergamot, cinnamon and **patchouli** essential oils makes a fresh, ultra-masculine soap.

Feet are not the most glamorous part of the body, but we would be lost without them, so it pays to heed the following advice. Take the time to **relax** your feet (see below), then massage the feet with this delicious combination of lemongrass, sage and rosemary essential oils in an ultra-moisturizing base. Sage will deal with any problems of sweatiness, while rosemary **revives** and, as a bonus, they are both great for relieving aches and pains. Lemongrass has an amazingly fresh aroma and will **stimulate** the circulation as well as being a **powerful** antiseptic and bactericide.

FOOTLOOSE FOOT LOTION

Ingredients

15 g (¹/₂ oz) beeswax

15 g (¹/₂ oz) cocoa butter

50 g (2 oz) coconut oil

30 ml (2 tbsp) sweet almond oil

60 ml (2 fl oz) mineral water

6 ml (1 tsp) lemongrass essential oil

2 ml (¹/₂ tsp) sage essential oil

2 ml (¹/₂ tsp) rosemary essential oil

Equipment

Stainless steel saucepan

Wooden spoon

Dark or clear glass jar with lid

Method

1 Place the beeswax and cocoa butter and the coconut and sweet almond oils in a heavy-bottomed stainless steel saucepan and melt slowly over a low heat. Thoroughly beat in the spring water with a wooden spoon until a smooth mixture is obtained.

2 Take the boiler off the heat and keep stirring until the cream has cooled to blood temperature. Add the essential oils and mix thoroughly.

3 Decant the cream to airtight jars and shake until the lotion has cooled completely, to stop the oil and water phases of the lotion separating while warm. Store clear glass jars in a dark place.

Massaging the feet

At the end of a tiring day, the best thing you can do is put your feet up, preferably by lying down with your feet higher than your heart, making sure that the whole leg is well supported. This greatly assists the circulation – including that of the lymphatic system – and relieves swelling and the feeling of heaviness in the legs. Very gentle massage towards the heart will increase the beneficial effect of raising the legs, using either the fingertips or a relaxed hand.

It is reputed that West African women tie **ginger** into their husbands' belts to **revive** their sexual prowess. Which is where the "What Women Want" bit comes from. We can't guarantee the effectiveness in this case, but the ginger in these bath salts will certainly revive any man who comes home from work and collapses in a chair in front of the television.

Lemongrass essential oil gives an instant lift and will wash any sticky sweatiness away. It also **soothes** headaches and stimulates the whole body. Just the thing after a hard day at work. These salts are very quick to make, and it is better to make a small quantity at a time so that they are always **fresh**.

"WHAT WOMEN WANT" BATH SALTS FOR MEN

Ingredients
5 ml (1 tsp) sweet almond oil

6 drops lemongrass essential oil

3 drops ginger essential oil

100 g (4 oz) Dead Sea salt

Equipment
Mixing bowl

Spoon

Dark or clear glass jars with lids

Method

1   Mix together the sweet almond oil and the essential oils, then stir in the Dead Sea salt. Pour into dark glass jars with lids, or keep clear glass jars in a dark place to protect the mix from the light.

2   Take a warm, refreshing bath with these energizing salts and see how much better you feel – one heaped teaspoonful added to your bath should do the trick. The salts are best used within a couple of months, but they are so good that we're sure they will be used up well before then.

These **wonderful** bath salts have a delicious feminine aroma, but needn't be exclusively for women. Why not share the bath!

Ylang ylang essential oil is wonderfully **relaxing** and is reputed to be aphrodisiac (certainly it is difficult not to feel sexy after smelling its alluring, exotic sweetness). Bergamot is the perfect companion to ylang ylang, because its sharp **citrus** aroma counteracts any heaviness, and its stimulant properties give you the energy to put all those **sexy** thoughts to good use. Say no more!

BACCHANALIAN BATH SALTS

Ingredients
5 ml (1 tsp) sweet almond oil
6 drops bergamot essential oil
3 drops ylang ylang essential oil
100 g (4 oz) Dead Sea salt

Equipment
Mixing bowl
Spoon
Dark or clear glass jars with lids

Method

1 Mix together the sweet almond oil and the essential oils, then stir in the Dead Sea salt. Pour into dark glass jars with lids or keep clear glass jars in a dark place to preserve the essential oils.

2 Add one heaped teaspoonful to the bath and enjoy.

Matching massage oil
You can also make a companion massage oil to gently smooth on after your bath and give a truly luxurious feeling. Mix the same amount of essential oils into 100 ml (4 fl oz) sweet almond oil. Pour into a dark glass bottle or store in clear glass in a dark place. Use after a bath or as a general body moisturizer.

Safety consideration
Bergamot essential oil makes the skin more sensitive to sunlight, so do not use it before exposing your skin to the sun.

BEAUTIFUL BODY SCRUB

Ingredients

250 g (9 oz) Dead Sea salt

125 ml (4 fl oz) sweet almond oil

5 ml (1 tsp) rosehip oil

3 drops lime essential oil

3 drops sweet orange essential oil

2 drops frankincense essential oil

1 drop clary sage essential oil

1 drop may chang essential oil

1 drop geranium essential oil

Equipment

Mixing bowl

Spoon

Dark or clear glass jars with tight-fitting lids

Method

1 Combine all the ingredients in a mixing bowl and spoon the scrub into jars. Keep clear glass jars in a dark place to protect the essential oils from the light.

2 Take a handful of the salt scrub and gently work it all over the body before rinsing off in a warm shower or bath, without using soap. Pat the skin dry with a soft towel and you will gain the full benefit of the oils, without any greasiness, and your skin will retain the delicate aroma of the essential oils.

Skin smoother
If you want to be really over-indulgent, why not add about a teaspoon of calendula oil to the mix. Calendula is renowned for its skin-smoothing properties and is one of the best all-round skin remedies.

There's nothing quite like an exfoliating scrub to leave your skin silky and smooth.

This exfoliating scrub features the perfect mixture of essential oils to condition and

soothe, deodorize and pamper, while the sweet almond and rosehip oils are readily

absorbed and will nourish the skin. The Dead Sea salt can be replaced with Maldon salt

flakes to make a gentler scrub for sensitive skin.

On a recent trip to Istanbul, I took my daughter to an ancient but fully functional Turkish bath. The time and ritual involved in thoroughly cleansing the body, followed by a full massage given by men and women – looking like wrestlers but with hands that were **gentle** and practised – **impressed** me beyond words. Even my daughter – who is very prudish – asked me the next day if we could repeat this experience.

That massage could only be complemented by using this ultra-feminine oil, that takes into consideration the whole person; mind, body and spirit.

Ylang ylang has a **calming** and relaxing effect and maybe this is the reason it is considered an aphrodisiac. Clary sage can be described as both **euphoric** and **relaxing**.

VENUS MASSAGE OIL

Ingredients
100 ml (4 fl oz) sweet almond oil

5 ml (1 tsp) ylang ylang essential oil

5 ml (1 tsp) clary sage essential oil

Equipment
Dark or clear glass bottle with lid

Method

1 Mix the sweet almond oil with the essential oils in a glass bottle. Store a clear glass bottle in a dark place to preserve the essential oils.

2 Let your partner massage the oil in all over.

The benefits of massage
Massage provides us with the most effective way of introducing essential oils to the body. The skin, our largest body organ, absorbs these oils, and when the whole body is massaged a considerable amount of essential oil can be taken into the bloodstream in a short time. The therapeutic benefits are quickly felt and the whole body is surrounded with the most delicious aroma.

Masks are particularly effective for **clearing** up blemishes, refining open pores and coarse skin, **nourishing**, healing and soothing the skin, as well as **exfoliating** the epidermis. But don't neglect the rest of your body. Dry elbows, knees, heels and throats will all **benefit** greatly from a mask.

HOME ALONE FACE MASKS

Citrus fruits are toning and antiseptic for all skin types, while strawberries soften the skin and combat oiliness in normal or combination skin. Tropical fruits, like pawpaw, pineapple and figs, are excellent exfoliants, without any scratchy bits. We normally choose organic fruits, which should be mashed and drained of any juices.

USING MASKS

Ideally, masks should be used on a face that has been deeply cleansed, and they should be applied to slightly damp skin, avoiding contact with the eyes. They should be left on for ten to thirty minutes – the individual recipes have their own suggested times – while you relax in a supine position. Make the most of this pleasurable experience by placing a pillow under your knees as well as one under your head, and listening to your favourite music.

Rinse the mask off with lukewarm water, or, even better, make a herbal infusion of lavatera, chamomile or lime tree leaves, let it cool to blood temperature and strain it (see page 20), then take off the mask by gently splashing the infusion over the skin.

Leave the face to dry naturally, or gently pat dry with a soft towel.

MASK FOR DRY SKIN

Honey is processed by bees from the nectar of flowers and has a natural quality that enhances its healing properties. It is very good for skin in need of moisture. Almonds soften and smooth the skin and apricots and peaches refine coarse skin.

Ingredients

2 ripe apricots or 1 ripe peach

2 tbsp runny honey

2 heaped tbsp ground almonds

Equipment

Sharp knife

Fork

Mixing bowl

Method

1 Peel, stone and mash the apricots or peach. Drain away any juices and then mix the mashed fruit with the honey and almonds.

2 Apply the mask to thoroughly cleansed skin, avoiding the eye area. Leave on for 20 to 30 minutes and rinse with lukewarm water or an infusion of lavatera or chamomile flowers.

MASK FOR OILY SKIN

With the tonic, astringent properties of lemons and the moisturizing and nourishing benefits of grapes, pear and egg white, which tightens the skin, this face mask is one of our favourites. You can also use it for combination skin on the appropriate areas.

Ingredients

1 egg white

Handful seedless white grapes or 1 large ripe pear

Juice of half a lemon

1 tsp bran

500 ml (18 fl oz) mineral water

10 drops witch hazel

Equipment

Mixing bowl

Fork

Sharp knife

Method

1 Beat the egg white until it forms soft white peaks, then peel and mash the grapes or pear, draining away any juices.

2 Mix the egg white with the lemon juice, bran and fruits. The mixture should be light and fluffy.

3 Gently massage this mask into the skin, paying particular attention to the nose, chin and forehead and avoiding the delicate eye area. Leave it on for about 15 minutes. Mix the mineral water and witch hazel and use it to rinse off the mask.

MASK FOR NORMAL SKIN

This mask is almost good enough to eat – the smell of strawberries makes it irresistible.

The wheatgerm oil is full of vitamin E for moisture and healing.

Ingredients

5–6 large, ripe strawberries

A handful of spearmint leaves

1 tsp wheatgerm oil

1 tsp orange juice

Equipment

Liquidizer

Method

1 Liquidize the strawberries and spearmint leaves then add the wheatgerm oil and orange juice.

2 Spread the mixture evenly on the face. For a complete summer feeling put two thin slices of peeled cucumber over your eyelids, then relax for 20 to 30 minutes. Rinse the mask off with lukewarm water or an infusion of lime tree leaves.

Nails show your state of health just as clearly as the condition of your skin, eyes or hair. So use this cream once a week to hide any secrets your hands may want to tell.

Lemon essential oil is great for treating brittle nails and has a brightening effect on the skin. Myrrh essential oil will help any fungal infection and is invaluable for **healing** chapped, irritated skin. Myrrh is reputed to have been carried by the Ancient Greeks as they went into battle, because of its strong **antiseptic** and wound healing properties. So it should have no problem sorting out torn cuticles.

REALLY CUTE CUTICLE CREAM

Ingredients
60 ml (2¹/₂ fl oz) mineral water

2 handfuls of young nettle tops

90 g (3¹/₂ oz) cocoa butter

20 g (³/₄ oz) glycerine

6 ml (1 tsp) lemon essential oil

2 ml (¹/₂ tsp) myrrh essential oil

Equipment
Measuring jug

Sieve

Stainless steel saucepan

Wooden spoon

Dark or clear glass jars with tight-fitting lids

Method

1 Infuse the nettle tops in boiling mineral water for 10 minutes (see page 20). Strain and allow to cool.

2 Melt the cocoa butter in a stainless steel saucepan over a low heat. Beat in the glycerine with a wooden spoon and slowly add the nettle infusion, stirring continuously.

3 Allow the cream to cool to blood temperature and add the essential oils. Spoon into airtight jars and shake until the lotion has cooled completely, to stop the oil and water phases separating while warm. Keep clear glass containers in a dark place to ensure the essential oils are well preserved.

4 Once a week, soak your hands in a warm infusion of lavatera and chamomile flowers. Take an orange stick with a cotton wool pad on the end and gently push back the cuticles. Then massage the nails with the Really Cute Cuticle Cream.

> **Safety consideration**
> Do not use myrrh while pregnant. Substitute with lavender essential oil for this recipe.

Dry chapped lips can be a nightmare, especially in the cold winter months, and mean that you won't be in the right frame of mind for kissing! Keep this lip salve with you at all times and pucker up!

KISS 'N' TELL LIP SALVE

ingredients
30 g (1 oz) beeswax

30 ml (2 tbsp) sweet almond oil

30 ml (2 tbsp) calendula oil

3 drops lavender essential oil

Equipment
Stainless steel saucepan

Wooden spoon

Small glass jar with lid

Method

1 Melt the almond oil and calendula oils and the beeswax together in a stainless steel saucepan over a low heat, stirring continuously.

2 When the beeswax has completely melted remove from the heat and continue to stir until the mixture cools to blood temperature.

3 Add the lavender oil and stir thoroughly. If you wish, you can add another essential oil to complement the lavender.

4 Transfer the mixture to a small glass jar and leave to set until cold.

GIFTWRAPPING IDEAS

The recipes in this chapter make perfect gifts – who wouldn't appreciate a gorgeously

wrapped pampering beauty product? Try putting one or two items in a gift box with some

shredded tissue paper or use sheer fabrics and shiny ribbons to add that special touch. A

handmade label in the shape of a heart is perfect for a bottle of Venus massage oil!

RELAX & REBALANCE

Here we have combined **elderflowers** with two of the most **fragrant** essential oils, the mineralized Dead Sea **salts** and rosehip oil to **pamper** the skin. It only takes a few minutes to put together this recipe so do try it.

HEARTS AND FLOWERS BATH SALTS

Ingredients
5 ml (1 tsp) rosehip oil

6 drops lime essential oil

3 drops geranium essential oil

100 g (4 oz) Dead Sea salt

A head of dried elderflowers

Equipment
Mixing bowl

Spoon

Dark or clear glass jars with lids

Method
1 Mix together the rosehip oil and the essential oils, then stir in the Dead Sea salt and elderflowers. Spoon into glass jars with lids, or keep clear glass jars in a dark place to protect the essential oils from the light.

2 Add a teaspoonful to the bath. These salts are better used when freshly made, so only store them for about a month for optimum results.

Elderflowers
Elderflowers are one of the beauties of the countryside, heralding the spring with their fresh, delicate aroma and dainty lace flowerheads. The flowers make wonderful cordial and, when dried, can be used to make a refreshing tea. Elder has a long history of use in creams and ointments. The flowers can be infused and added to creams for use on hands and body, or a few fresh flowers mixed with live yogurt make a great face pack to clear the skin and prevent wrinkles.

This **therapeutic** massage oil induces deep sleep and eases the aches and pains of the day. Thyme is an amazing essential oil because it is used to stimulate the circulation, **ease** fatigue and **soothe** rheumatic pains, and it is one of the best oils to use for insomnia because of its **balancing** effect on the nervous system. Combined with sweet orange essential oil, which has sedative properties, and juniper berry essential oil, which will **detoxify** the body overnight, you'll be asleep before the massage ends.

THYMELESS SLEEP OIL

Ingredients
100 ml (4 fl oz) sweet almond oil

8 drops thyme essential oil

8 drops sweet orange essential oil

4 drops juniper berry essential oil

Equipment
Dark or clear glass bottle with tight-fitting lid

Method

1 Mix all the oils together in a dark bottle with a tight-fitting lid, or store a clear bottle in the dark to preserve the oil.

2 Use as a massage oil before bed. Even a little rubbed into the hands and arms will help you sleep.

Safety considerations
Avoid juniper berry and thyme essential oils while pregnant. For this recipe use lavender instead.

If you suffer from nut allergies, you should replace the sweet almond oil with grapeseed or sunflower oil.

While most men do not have a specific facial cleansing routine, we think they'll **love** this facial soap with **exfoliating** properties to unblock pores and deep cleanse the skin, leaving the face moisturized and smooth. The aroma of Boy Oh Boy is fruity but with a deep undertone of cinnamon spice. A **warming**, stimulant essential oil, cinnamon is ideal for a masculine soap when combined with citrus aromas. Grapefruit and sweet orange essential oils have been added for their "**sunshine**" aromas that lift the spirits and soothe the skin. Sprinkle poppy seeds in the finished soap to give gentle exfoliation and an interesting texture.

BOY OH BOY SCRUB SOAP FOR MEN

Ingredients

170 ml (6 fl oz) sunflower oil

170 ml (6 fl oz) olive oil

155 g (5 oz) coconut oil

65 g (2¹/₂ oz) caustic soda

230 ml (8 fl oz) mineral water

10 ml (2 tsp) grapefruit essential oil

6 ml (1 tsp) sweet orange essential oil

4 ml (1 tsp) cinnamon leaf essential oil

2 tbsp poppy seeds

Equipment

General equipment (see page 12)

Safety equipment (see page 13)

Wooden board

Tray

Method

1 Work in a well-ventilated area. Oil and line a plastic mould with greaseproof paper.

2 Melt the sunflower, olive and coconut oils in a large, heavy-based stainless steel saucepan over a low heat.

3 Wearing protective goggles, a mask, an apron and long rubber gloves, add the caustic soda to the mineral water in a plastic bucket and stir with a plastic spatula until dissolved.

4 Using one jam thermometer for the oils and another for the caustic soda mixture (lye water), allow both temperatures to reach 35.5°C (96°F) – you may need to reheat the oils. Wearing protective clothing, immediately pour the lye water into the oils, off the heat. Combine the mixtures thoroughly using the spatula. Continuously stir for approximately 15 minutes.

5 Tracing occurs when a drizzle of the mixture on the surface of the soap leaves a visible line. At this point add the essential oils and poppy seeds and combine thoroughly. Pour into the prepared mould and place in a safe, warm, dry place for 24 hours, covering with cardboard to keep the heat in.

6 Wearing protective gloves, turn out the soap onto a wooden board covered with greaseproof paper. Peel off the lining paper and cut the soap into the desired shapes using a carving knife or biscuit cutters. If the mixture is too soft to cut, leave for a further 24 hours. Space out the cut soaps on a tray lined with greaseproof paper and leave in a dark, warm, dry place for four weeks, turning several times during the maturing process.

This **dreamy**, creamy lotion to stroke all over is enriching for both your physical and psychological self. Your **body** will be eternally grateful for its **moisture** treat and the combination of two **super-relaxing** essential oils.

DREAMBOAT ALL-OVER NIGHT CREAM

Ingredients
15 g (¹/₂ oz) beeswax

15 g (¹/₂ oz) cocoa butter

50 g (2 oz) coconut oil

30 ml (2 tbsp) sweet almond oil

60 ml (4 tbsp) mineral water

6 ml (1 tsp) lavender essential oil

*4 ml (1 tsp) ylang ylang
essential oil*

Equipment
Stainless steel saucepan

Wooden spoon

Dark or clear glass jar with lid

Method

1 Place the beeswax, cocoa butter, coconut oil and sweet almond oil in a large, heavy-based stainless steel saucepan and melt slowly over a low heat. Beat the mineral water in vigorously with a wooden spoon.

2 Take the pan off the heat and keep stirring until the cream has cooled to blood temperature. Add the essential oils and mix thoroughly. Pour into airtight jars and shake until cool to prevent the water and oil phases separating while warm. Keep clear jars in a dark place to preserve the essential oils.

3 Rub the cream in all over the body as part of your bedtime routine, and look forward to golden dreams

TANGERINE DREAM SOAP

Ingredients

300 ml (10 fl oz) extra-virgin olive oil

100 ml (4 fl oz) sweet almond oil

65 g (2¹/₂ oz) coconut oil

60 g (2¹/₂ oz) palm oil

40 g (1¹/₂ oz) beeswax

65 g (2¹/₂ oz) caustic soda

230 ml (8 fl oz) mineral water

10 ml (2 tsp) tangerine essential oil

5 ml (1 tsp) sweet orange essential oil

5 ml (1 tsp) lavender essential oil

Equipment

General equipment (see page 12)

Safety equipment (see page 13)

Wooden board

Tray

Method

1 Work in a well-ventilated area. Oil and line a plastic mould with greaseproof paper.

2 Melt the olive, sweet almond, coconut and palm oils with the beeswax in a large, heavy-based stainless steel saucepan over a low heat.

3 Wearing protective eyewear, a face mask, an apron and long rubber gloves, pour the caustic soda into the mineral water in a plastic bucket and stir with a plastic spatula until completely dissolved.

4 Using two jam thermometers, one for the oils and one for the caustic soda mixture (lye water), monitor both solutions until they equalize at 55°C (131°F). At this point, while still wearing the protective clothing, pour the lye water into the oils and stir thoroughly, continuing to stir until the mixture traces – when a drizzle of mixture leaves a line on the surface of the soap.

5 Pour in the essential oils and mix thoroughly, then pour the soap into the prepared mould. Cover with cardboard and leave in a safe, warm, dry place for 24 hours.

6 Wearing gloves – the soap is still caustic at this stage – turn out the soap onto a board lined with greaseproof paper. Remove the lining paper and cut the soaps to the desired size with a carving knife. Space the soaps out on a tray covered with greaseproof paper and store for four weeks in a warm, dry place, turning occasionally.

7 Use this soap in a leisurely bath to really appreciate its magic.

Achieving a **balance** is what aromatherapy is all about, and it's what we would all love to have in our lives too. This soap balances the wonderful **relaxing** and sedative powers of lavender and sweet orange with the fresh, lively aroma of tangerine essential oil. This is a **gentle**, unassuming soap with lashings of extra-virgin olive oil, sweet almond oil and coconut oil to look after your skin.

We have developed this face cream to tackle the effects of age on the skin. In skincare, frankincense is particularly helpful for older skin. It helps restore tone to facial skin and slows down the appearance of wrinkles. It may even reduce the extent of wrinkles that have already formed. Lemon juice clears the skin and, used in a face lotion, helps banish wrinkles. While lemon essential oil has a brightening effect on sallow skin and age spots, aids the circulation and has a mild bleaching effect. The calendula infusion will add to the soothing effect of this cream and is useful for dryness and flakiness.

MOONSHADOW FACIAL NIGHT CREAM

Ingredients

A handful of dried calendula flowers

20 g ($^3/_4$ oz) beeswax

20 ml (1 fl oz) calendula oil

40 ml (1$^1/_2$ fl oz) sweet almond oil

10 ml (2 tsp) lemon juice

3 ml ($^1/_2$ tsp) frankincense essential oil

1 ml ($^1/_4$ tsp) lemon essential oil

Equipment

Measuring jug

Sieve

Stainless steel saucepan

Wooden spoon

Dark or clear glass jars with lids

Method

1 Make a herbal infusion with the calendula flowers and 300 ml (10 fl oz) boiling water (see page 20). Strain and set aside to cool.

2 Melt the beeswax in a large, heavy-based stainless steel saucepan. Add the oils, beating steadily with a wooden spoon, then add 30 ml (2 tbsp) of the calendula infusion and the lemon juice in a slow trickle.

3 Take the saucepan off the heat and continue to stir until the lotion has cooled to blood temperature. Add the essential oils, then decant the cream into jars and shake until the lotion has completely cooled. If you are using clear glass jars, keep them in a dark place away from direct sunlight to preserve the essential oils.

4 Before bed, cleanse the face then gently smooth on the night cream working upwards from jaw to cheekbones, around the eyes and over the forehead. Work the cream into the neck from the base to the chin.

It is no accident that so many of the essential oils regarded as

antidepressants are the product of summer flowers, such as

lavender, jasmine and geranium. At a deep subconscious level they

evoke **warm** breezes, **sunny** days, summer gardens, holidays and

happy memories. Citrus oils, particularly bergamot, can also be

used to lift your mood if you are stressed or unhappy.

EMOTIONAL RESCUE MASSAGE OIL

Ingredients
100 ml (4 fl oz) sweet almond oil

4 ml (1 tsp) lavender essential oil

4 ml (1 tsp) bergamot essential oil

2 ml ($\frac{1}{2}$ tsp) lemongrass essential oil

Equipment
Plastic jug

Wooden spoon

Dark or clear glass bottle with tight-fitting lid

Method

1 Measure the sweet almond oil in a plastic jug then add the essential oils, stirring continuously.

2 Pour the massage oil into a bottle and fix the lid. Keep a clear glass bottle in a dark place to preserve the essential oils.

3 Immediately before use, gently shake the bottle to mix the oils well. Always keep light, relaxed hands when massaging, unless you are properly trained. A gentle massage is much more soothing and if you are not an expert you can do real damage by being heavy handed.

The benefits of massage
After a long, stressful week, heal and restore yourself by massaging on either side of the spine with Emotional Rescue Massage Oil, then let your mind drift away to peace and calm. Massage almost always brings about muscular relaxation, even without the use of essential oils, though the combination of the two can have a dramatic effect.

Safety consideration
Bergamot essential oil should not be used on the skin before it is exposed to sunshine, since it makes the skin more sensitive to sunlight.

A small pouch filled with dried flowers can be placed inside your usual pillowcase to relax your mind and send you off to sleep. The therapeutic benefits of the plants used depend very much on the way they are gathered and dried. Flowers should be gathered in dry weather, once the sun has risen and the dew has cleared. Leaves should be gathered before they are fully developed. To ensure the dried plants conserve their active constituents at a maximum they should be dried in the sun, a greenhouse, a drying cupboard or in the oven.

SWEET DREAMS HERBAL PILLOWS

Ingredients

Dried flowers: for a peaceful sleep try hops, cowslips, lemon balm and lavender

Equipment

Muslin or a loose-woven fabric

Scissors

Ribbon

Method

1 Cut out a piece of fabric, approximately 20 cm (8 in) square, and place the dried flower mixture in the centre. Gather up the edges of the fabric and tie a pretty ribbon around the neck of the pouch to hold the flowers in. Allow room for the dried plants to "breathe" and to release their therapeutic aroma.

2 Tuck a pouch in the corner of your pillowcase and drift away on a fragrant cloud.

Just like a breath of **fresh** air, bracing and invigorating, this soap also has the wonderful scent of the **sea** (but without the fish!). We've added seaweed for texture and nutrients, sage essential oil for its antifungal properties and petitgrain for the skin. Grapefruit essential oil **refreshes** and uplifts, while orange essential oil has a **calming** and balancing effect.

SEA AIR BODY SOAP

Ingredients

225 ml (8 fl oz) olive oil

40 ml (1$^{1}/_{2}$ fl oz) avocado oil

50 g (2 oz) coconut oil

50 g (2 oz) palm oil

30 g (1 oz) beeswax

180 ml (6$^{1}/_{2}$ fl oz) mineral water

55 g (2 oz) caustic soda

7 ml (1$^{1}/_{2}$ tsp) grapefruit essential oil

6 ml (1 tsp) sweet orange essential oil

2 ml ($^{1}/_{2}$ tsp) petitgrain essential oil

1 ml ($^{1}/_{4}$ tsp) sage essential oil

2 handfuls of arame seaweed

Equipment

General equipment (see page 12)

Safety equipment (see page 13)

Wooden board

Tray

Method

1 Work in a well-ventilated area. First oil and line a plastic mould with greasproof paper.

2 Melt the olive oil, avocado oil, coconut oil, palm oil and beeswax in a large heavy-based stainless steel saucepan over a low heat.

3 Using protective eyewear, apron and long rubber gloves pour the caustic soda into the mineral water in a plastic bucket, stirring continuously with a plastic spatula to dissolve.

4 Using a separate thermometer for the oils and the caustic soda mixture (lye water), monitor both solutions until they reach 55°C (131°F). Still wearing the protective clothing, immediately pour the lye water into the oils and stir thoroughly. Continue stirring until "tracing" occurs (see page 11).

5 Add the essential oils, stirring well until they are thoroughly combined with the soap mixture and then do the same with the seaweed. Pour the soap into the prepared mould, and make a "wave" pattern on the top of the soap using a spoon or a spatula. Leave to set for 24 hours, covered with cardboard in a warm, dry place.

6 Wearing protective gloves, turn the soap out onto a wooden board covered with greaseproof paper and cut, wave side up, into chunky bars. Space the bars out on a tray lined with greaseproof paper. Leave to cure in a warm, dry place for four weeks.

GIFTWRAPPING IDEAS

Blue, the colour of the sea and the sky, is wonderfully calming and relaxing – perfect for wrapping up some of the soaps and other items in this chapter. A glass bottle wrapped in soft muslin and tied with a purple ribbon makes an elegant gift, while a smart checked ribbon smartens up a simple pot of face cream. For a special gift, place a handmade soap on a shell soap dish and tie with pretty blue ribbon.

RESTORE & HEAL

"Stop the world, I want to get off!" Whether it's you or a friend in crisis, this **delicious** mixture will help soothe troubled emotions and relieve some of the tension. Juniper berry is an **amazing** essential oil in that it's cleansing, detoxifying properties work on the mind as well as the body, **reviving** the emotionally drained. Bergamot has the most delightful citrus aroma and immediately uplifts the spirits, making it the ideal companion for juniper berry. The result will leave you **refreshed**, lively and ready for anything.

STOP THE WORLD DE-STRESS OIL

Ingredients
30 ml (2 tbsp) sweet almond oil

8 drops bergamot essential oil

4 drops juniper berry essential oil

Equipment
Dark or clear glass bottle with tight-fitting lid

Method
1 Mix all the ingredients thoroughly in a bottle with a tight-fitting lid. Keep clear glass in the dark to preserve the essential oils.

2 Ideally, this oil should be used in conjunction with a wonderful massage, but if that isn't possible, just smooth it onto arms, legs, hands, feet, or whatever part of the body is accessible at the time.

> ### Safety considerations
> Pregnant women, who we hope won't be stressed, should in any case replace the juniper berry essential oil in this recipe with lavender.
>
> Bergamot essential oil makes the skin more sensitive to sunlight, so do not use it if you are likely to be exposed to the sun.

ANGEL HAIR THERAPEUTIC SHAMPOO BAR

Ingredients

270 ml (9 fl oz) mineral water

2 chamomile teabags

700 ml (1¼ pints) olive oil

90 ml (3½ fl oz) sweet almond oil

60 g (2 oz) beeswax

55 g (2 oz) creamed coconut

110 g (4 oz) caustic soda

20 ml (4 tsp) bergamot essential oil

10 ml (2 tsp) lavender essential oil

5 ml (1 tsp) geranium essential oil

5 ml (1 tsp) rosemary essential oil

Equipment

General equipment (see page 12)

Safety equipment (see page 13)

Sieve

Wooden board

Tray

Method

1 Boil the mineral water and pour over the chamomile teabags in a bowl. Leave to cool then strain, reserving the infusion.

2 Work in a well-ventilated area. First oil and line a plastic mould with greaseproof paper.

3 Melt the olive and sweet almond oils with the beeswax and coconut cream in a stainless steel saucepan over a low heat, stirring regularly so that the coconut cream does not "catch" the bottom of the pan and burn.

4 Wearing protective gloves, goggles, a face mask and an apron, pour the caustic soda into the chamomile infusion in a plastic bucket, to make the lye water. Stir with a plastic spatula to dissolve.

5 Using one jam thermometer for the oils and one for the lye water, monitor both mixtures until they reach 55°C (131°F). Still wearing the protective clothing, immediately pour the lye water into the oils and mix thoroughly, stirring until tracing occurs – when a drizzle of the mixture makes a line on the surface of the soap.

6 Add the essential oils and mix well. Pour the soap into the prepared mould, cover with cardboard and leave for 24 hours in a safe, warm, dry place.

7 The soap is still caustic at this stage so wear protective gloves while you turn out the soap onto a wooden board covered with greaseproof paper. Peel off the lining paper and cut the bar into the desired shapes using a carving knife. Space the cut soaps out well on a tray covered with greaseproof paper and store in a dry, warm place for four weeks, turning occasionally to dry evenly.

> ### Recycling the teabags
> Save the chamomile teabags after you have made the infusion. They are great for soothing tired eyes when laid over the eyelids for five minutes.

We've come up with a combination that we think is the **ultimate** treatment for hair. A creamy, conditioning shampoo bar to **revive** flagging (and thinning) locks. It has a delectable aroma to boot! As my friend's four-year-old said to me (Cheryl) as I piggy-backed him along the beach, "your hair smells of **strawberries** and **peaches**!" Well, he may not have been accurate on the content, but there cannot be many greater compliments!

Many headaches are caused by tension, and the best way of **relieving** them is to lie down with one pillow under your head and another under your knees, and apply a cold (not icy), essential oil compress to the forehead for ten minutes. Not only does this help a headache, but it is also extremely **soothing** in the case of fever.

The definitive headache essential oil is lavender, and even a drop dabbed on each temple can be **effective**, and just as quick as taking a painkiller. Peppermint is excellent for a "sick" headache and rosemary and eucalyptus are **perfect** for a "blocked sinus" headache. A combination of lemon and lavender essential oils will also reduce fever.

HEAD TO HEAD COMPRESS

Ingredients

Cold water

Essential oils, such as lavender, lemon, peppermint, rosemary or eucalyptus

Equipment

Large bowl

Face flannel

Method

1 Take a large bowl of cold, but not icy, water, and sprinkle in a couple of drops of essential oil. Swirl a face flannel in the water and gently wring it out.

2 Place the flannel over the forehead and leave for ten minutes. Ideally you also need an understanding helper to soak and wring the flannel to refresh it as necessary when it warms up. The combination of relaxation, cooling and the therapeutic effect of the essential oils will calm and soothe.

Migraines – another story altogether

Migraines, like tension headaches, may well be triggered by, among other things, stress. However, any sufferer will tell you that the last thing they want during an attack is to be near a strong smell, even a lovely essential oil. So, for migraine sufferers, prevention is the best form of cure. We suggest using one or more of the recipes featured in the Relax & Rebalance chapter on a regular basis, to keep tension at bay.

Although often neglected, our feet need a little **tender** loving care too. Cramped and often hot – and smelly – they deserve a **treat** as good as this lemon and ginger night cream.

Lemon essential oil is an excellent skin conditioner for the feet, and it treats verrucas, tender feet, brittle nails, chilblains and generally disinfects and **freshens** the feet. Ginger essential oil will zing the circulation and relieve those tired, achy feelings that feet inevitably suffer from after a hard day.

SOLE TO SOLE NIGHT CREAM FOR FEET

Ingredients

15 g (¹/₂ oz) beeswax

15 g (¹/₂ oz) cocoa butter

50 g (2 oz) coconut oil

30 ml (2 tbsp) sweet almond oil

60 ml (4 tbsp) mineral water

7 ml (1¹/₂ tsp) lemon essential oil

3 ml (¹/₂ tsp) ginger essential oil

Equipment

Stainless saucepan

Wooden spoon

Dark or clear glass jars with lids

Method

1 Place the beeswax, cocoa butter and coconut and sweet almond oils in a large, heavy-based stainless steel saucepan and melt over a low heat. Add the mineral water in a gentle trickle and beat with a wooden spoon until a smooth mixture is obtained.

2 Take the saucepan off the heat and keep stirring until the cream has cooled to blood temperature. Add the essential oils and mix thoroughly.

3 Decant the cream to airtight jars and shake until the lotion has cooled completely, to stop the oil and water phases of the cream separating while warm. Store clear glass jars in a dark place to preserve the essential oils.

4 Close to bedtime, take a warm bath then smooth or gently massage a generous amount of cream into the feet. Put on a pair of cotton socks and allow the treatment to work overnight.

Many of us put our hands through a great deal of abuse: hard work, cold weather and harsh detergents all take their toll. Cuts, irritations, brittle and split nails and dry and cracked skin are common complaints. But help is at hand from this **nourishing** cream. Lemon essential oil is invaluable for its antiseptic and anti-ageing properties, as well as having a mild bleaching effect, useful for stains and liver spots. Lavender will **soothe** even the most irritated of skin and stimulate the healing of cuts and cracks, burns and stings.

HEALING HANDS NIGHT CREAM

Ingredients

15 g (¹/₂ oz) beeswax

15 g (¹/₂ oz) cocoa butter

50 g (2 oz) coconut oil

30 ml (2 tbsp) vitamin E oil or wheatgerm oil

60 ml (4 tbsp) mineral water

6 ml (1 tsp) lavender essential oil

4 ml (1 tsp) lemon essential oil

Equipment

Stainless steel saucepan

Wooden spoon

Dark or clear glass jars with lids

Method

1 Melt the beeswax, cocoa butter and coconut and vitamin E or wheatgerm oils in a large, heavy-based stainless saucepan over a low heat. Add the mineral water in a gentle trickle and beat thoroughly with a wooden spoon.

2 Take the saucepan off the heat and keep stirring until the cream has cooled to blood temperature. Add the essential oils and mix thoroughly.

3 Decant the cream to airtight jars and shake until the cream has cooled completely, to stop the oil and water phases separating while warm. Store clear glass jars in a dark place to protect the mix from the light.

4 This rich, nourishing cream is best massaged generously into hands, nails and cuticles and then left overnight, wearing pure cotton gloves to aid absorption.

YOU'RE SO VEIN VARICOSE VEIN CREAM

Ingredients

200 g (7 oz) cocoa butter

30 g (1 oz) coconut oil

20 ml ($^3/_4$ fl oz) calendula oil

2 handfuls of calendula plants, flowers, stems and leaves

15 drops juniper berry essential oil

15 drops lemon essential oil

Equipment

Stainless steel saucepan

Wooden spoon

Muslin

Dark or clear glass jars with lids

Method

1 Melt the cocoa butter and coconut and calendula oils in a large, heavy-based stainless steel saucepan over a low heat.

2 Place the calendula plants in the hot oil mixture and stir well with a wooden spoon. It will appear frothy. Remove from the heat, cover and leave overnight.

3 The next day, reheat the cream until it melts, then strain it through muslin to remove the calendula plants. Mix in the essential oils. Pour the cream into glass jars and allow to cool completely. Keep clear jars in a dark place to preserve the essential oils.

Avoiding varicose veins

The best advice to avoid the onset of varicose veins is to rest with your legs higher than your heart whenever you have the opportunity, take regular exercise and avoid standing for any length of time. Don't cross your legs or sit with your feet tucked under you, because this cuts off the circulation. Be careful when massaging varicose veins – don't apply direct pressure and use light stroking movements. Always stroke upwards, towards the heart. If in doubt, ask a professional or just smooth the cream gently over the affected areas.

You could also try this calendula tincture. Infuse a small handful of calendula petals in 50 ml (2 fl oz) vodka (see page 20). Cover and leave for 14 days in a warm place, shaking daily. Strain and add 100 ml (4 fl oz) witch hazel. When cool, dab onto the affected areas.

Safety consideration

Do not use juniper berry essential oil while pregnant. Instead, lavender essential oil is a good substitute in this recipe.

Varicose veins are a common problem that affect many men as well as women. Often achy or downright painful, anything that can help to ease them is welcome. This gentle cream contains calendula, a marvellous plant with many and varied virtues, none less than its use in the healing of skin and treatment of varicose veins. Juniper berry essential oil is wonderfully detoxifying and helps to alleviate fluid retention, which goes hand in hand with varicose veins and poor circulation. It is also valuable in maintaining the condition of the skin.

Chamomile essential oil is well known for its soothing, **calming** and anti-inflammatory qualities and is used for many skin problems, particularly where there is sensitivity, dryness and irritation. This includes conditions such as eczema and urticaria, where the calming and **stress relieving** properties are also helpful. We have also added myrrh essential oil to this cream, for its antifungal action. So, if you have overdone the gardening or housework, perhaps using strong detergents or getting stung by nettles, try this **soothing** balm.

CHAMOMILE SOOTHER FOR IRRITATED HAND

Ingredients
2 handfuls of chamomile flowers

250 ml (9 fl oz) water

40 ml (1^1/$_2$ fl oz) sweet almond oil

30 g (1 oz) beeswax

1^1/$_2$ tbsp clear honey

20 ml (^{3}/$_4$ fl oz) wheatgerm oil

5 drops Roman chamomile essential oil

5 drops myrrh essential oil

Equipment
Saucepan with lid

Coffee filter paper

Stainless steel saucepan

Wooden spoon

Dark or clear glass jars with lids

Method

1 Make a chamomile infusion by gently simmering the chamomile flowers in the water in a saucepan with a lid for 30 minutes. Leave covered and allow to cool.

2 Strain through a coffee filter paper and retain the liquid.

3 Melt the almond oil and beeswax together in a large, heavy-based stainless steel saucepan. Add the honey and stir into the mixture with a wooden spoon. Add the wheatgerm oil and herbal infusion and beat thoroughly.

4 Take the saucepan off the heat and keep stirring until the cream has cooled to blood temperature. Add the essential oils and mix thoroughly, stirring slowly until the cream is cool.

5 Pour the cream into glass jars and keep clear glass jars in a dark place to preserve the oils.

6 Use this superb soothing cream in small quantities, paying special attention to the cuticles.

> **Safety consideration**
> If you are pregnant substitute the myrrh essential oil with lavender.

Stretch marks can be an unfortunate after-effect of pregnancy. However, we have the answer and our cream will soon have you feeling yummy and glamorous again. The essential oils of lavender and lemon have a healing effect on the skin and reduce the redness of the marks, optimizing the skin's regenerative powers. Ylang ylang essential oil is a great skin conditioner and also a powerful aphrodisiac, which will help you to feel sexy again.

YUMMY MUMMY STRETCH MARK CREAM

Ingredients

15 g (¹/₂ oz) beeswax

15 g (¹/₂ oz) cocoa butter

50 g (2 oz) coconut oil

30 ml (2 tbsp) evening primrose oil

60 ml (4 tbsp) mineral water

5 ml (1 tsp) ylang ylang essential oil

3 ml (¹/₂ tsp) lavender essential oil

2 ml (¹/₂ tsp) lemon essential oil

Equipment

Stainless steel saucepan

Wooden spoon

Dark or clear glass jars with lids

Method

1 Melt the beeswax, cocoa butter and coconut and evening primrose oils in a large, heavy-based stainless steel saucepan over a low heat. Beat in the spring water with a wooden spoon until you have a smooth mixture.

2 Take the saucepan off the heat and keep stirring until the cream has cooled to blood temperature. Add the essential oils and mix thoroughly to make a smooth cream.

3 Decant the cream to airtight jars and shake until the lotion has cooled completely, to stop the oil and water phases separating while warm. Store clear glass jars in a dark place to ensure the essential oils are well preserved.

4 Gently smooth the cream into the skin over the offending area. Use daily after a bath or shower and your skin will feel softer after just a few days.

Asian cultures have used hair oils for centuries, and know the benefits of head massage to relax the large flat muscles over the scalp, the forehead (where a lot of tension develops) and the base of the skull (the focal point for stress). As well as relaxing the mind and body, the rosemary and lemongrass essential oils will rejuvenate your hair while lavender and geranium essential oils will treat a flaky scalp.

Good circulation is all-important for healthy hair. So give your head a real treat, or even better ask a friend or partner with firm, but gentle fingers to massage for you! Leave the oil on overnight if you can, wearing a towelling "turban" to protect the pillow. Wash with a gentle shampoo and dry as normal.

HAIR HEAVEN

Ingredients
100 ml (4 fl oz) sweet almond oil or light olive oil

3 ml ($^1/_2$ tsp) geranium essential oil

3 ml ($^1/_2$ tsp) lavender essential oil

3 ml ($^1/_2$ tsp) lemongrass essential oil

3 ml ($^1/_2$ tsp) rosemary essential oil

Equipment
Dark or clear glass bottle with tight-fitting lid

Method
1 Put all the oils in a bottle with a tight lid and shake well. Store clear glass in a dark cupboard, away from little ones.

2 Use before bed. Shake the bottle well, pour about a tablespoon into the palm of your hand and massage well into the scalp. Leave overnight and shampoo out the following morning.

3 Repeat weekly to keep your hair and scalp in good condition.

SIX PACK SOAP

Ingredients

100 ml (4 fl oz) mineral water

2 handfuls of lavatera flowers and stems

A handful of chamomile flowers

130 ml (4$\frac{1}{2}$ fl oz) olive oil

25 g (1 oz) palm oil

25 g (1 oz) coconut oil

15 g ($\frac{1}{2}$ oz) beeswax

25 g (1 oz) caustic soda

10 ml (2 tsp) bergamot essential oil

8 ml (1$\frac{1}{2}$ tsp) clary sage essential oil

2 ml ($\frac{1}{2}$ tsp) lavender essential oil

2 ml ($\frac{1}{2}$ tsp) patchouli essential oil

Equipment

General equipment (see page 12)

Safety equipment (see page 13)

Method

1 Boil the mineral water with the chamomile and lavatera flowers and stems for two minutes. Allow to cool and then strain, reserving the infusion and flowers. Make up the volume to 100 ml (4 fl oz) with more mineral water if necessary.

2 Work in a well-ventilated area. First oil and line a plastic mould with greaseproof paper.

3 Melt the olive, palm and coconut oils with the beeswax in a stainless steel saucepan over a low heat.

4 Wearing rubber gloves, an apron and protective eyewear and a mask, pour the caustic soda into the chamomile and lavatera infusion in a plastic bucket. Stir until dissolved with a plastic spatula.

5 Using two jam thermometers, one for the oil and one for the caustic soda mix (lye water), allow both solutions to reach 55°C (131°F). Still wearing the protective clothing, immediately pour the lye water into the oil mixture and stir well to thoroughly incorporate the two. Continue to stir well until the mixture traces – when a drizzle leaves a line on the surface of the soap. Pour in the essential oils and a handful of the infused flowers and stir well again.

6 Pour the soap into the prepared mould. Cover with cardboard and leave for 24 hours in a dry, safe, warm place.

7 Remember that the soap is still caustic at this stage, so wear rubber gloves to handle it. Turn out the soap onto a wooden board covered with greaseproof paper, remove the lining paper and cut to the desired sizes with a carving knife. Arrange the soaps on a tray covered with greaseproof paper and allow to mature for four weeks in a dry, warm place, turning occasionally to assist the drying.

> **Safety consideration**
> Bergamot essential oil makes the skin more sensitive to sunlight, so do not use it before being exposed to the sun.

This is quite a masculine soap, however that is not to say that women won't enjoy using it too.

Clary sage essential oil has a wonderfully **nutty** aroma – it also prevents excessive sweating.

Patchouli, with its antiseptic qualities, also acts as a fixative for the other essential oils and

gives an **exotic** scent to this soap. Lavender has a list of attributes as long as your arm: in this

soap it balances the other oils. Bergamot blends nicely with these essential oils and prevents

sleepiness. It is a cheering, **uplifting** essential oil and adds a lovely citrus top note to the aroma.

Painful joints will love the feel of a **gentle** rub with this oil. Lavender and rosemary essential oils will ease the aching and juniper berry oil is well known to improve the circulation and **detoxify** the body. Remember that pregnant women should avoid juniper berry essential oil – simply replace with another of your **favourite** oils.

(OH, MY) POOR OLD BONES JOINT OIL

Ingredients

50 ml (2 fl oz) sweet almond oil

6 drops lavender essential oil

4 drops juniper berry essential oil

2 drops rosemary essential oil

Equipment

Dark or clear glass bottle with tight-fitting lid

Method

1 Mix all the ingredients together in a bottle with a tight-fitting lid. Store a clear glass bottle in a dark place to preserve the essential oils.

2 Warmth is a great relief for arthritic joints, so rub this in after a warm bath for maximum effect, then wear something loose, like a tracksuit or pyjamas, and relax with your body well supported.

This is a wonderfully balancing facial oil for all skin types. Rosehip oil is the finest base oil for **delicate** skin and is readily absorbed with no greasiness. Geranium essential oil balances sebum production and **nourishes** dry or combination skins. Ylang ylang is the most feminine and sensual of all essential oils and, like geranium, it **balances** the skin, making it suitable for dry or combination skins.

FABULOUS FACIAL OIL

Ingredients
100 ml (4 fl oz) rosehip oil

10 drops ylang ylang essential oil

4 drops geranium essential oil

Equipment
Dark or clear glass bottle with tight-fitting lid

Method

1 Place all the ingredients in a bottle and shake gently to combine. If you are using a clear glass bottle, store in a dark place to preserve the essential oils.

2 Use this oil nightly, before going to bed, to allow the oil to fully absorb into your skin while you sleep for an ultra-conditioning effect. Apply to warm, thoroughly cleansed skin.

Rosehips
Rosehip oil is a natural preservative which also eases inflammation. Rosehips have other uses too – long before the discovery of vitamin C, rosehip tea was taken to combat the common cold.

At some time we all catch too much sun and are left feeling pink and sore. When that happens, use this oil to calm and **soothe** both you and your skin. Lavender essential oil has powerful healing properties, having been proved effective in treating even severe burns, it is antiseptic and will **calm** the inflammation and ease the pain associated with sunburn. Chamomile essential oil also soothes the inflammation and has a calming effect on the body, aiding **relaxation** and sleep.

WHAT A SCORCHER SUNBURN OIL

Ingredients

30 ml (2 tbsp) sweet almond oil

6 drops lavender essential oil

2 drops Roman chamomile essential oil

Equipment

Dark or clear glass bottle with tight-fitting lid

Method

1 Place all the ingredients in a bottle with a tight-fitting lid, shake well and store clear glass in a dark place to preserve the essential oils.

2 If you can't bear to smooth the oil onto your skin, a few drops of the mixture run into a tepid bath is of great relief. Pat dry with a soft towel and wear soft, loose clothes to avoid rubbing the skin.

Traditional sunburn remedy
If you don't have the ingredients for this recipe to hand, try mixing two teaspoons of tomato juice and four tablespoons of buttermilk and applying to the affected area. Leave for half an hour, then wash off.

GIFTWRAPPING IDEAS

The natural look is perfect for wrapping some of the healing products from this chapter – and can look just as smart. Wooden or cardboard boxes can be filled with shredded tissue or raffia while a bundle of cinnamon sticks or a slice or dried fruit adds a special touch. Skeleton leaves or pieces of bark can be wrapped around a soap and tied with raffia.

SUPPLIERS & USEFUL ADDRESSES

UNITED KINGDOM

Essentially Oils
8–10 Mount Farm
Junction Road
Churchill
Chipping Norton
Oxfordshire OX7 6NP
Tel: (01608) 659544
Fax: (01608) 659566
Email: sales@essentiallyoils.com
www.essentiallyoils.com
*Suppliers of essential oils,
carrier oils, bottles, jars and
other soapmaking essentials.*

Holland & Barrett
Samuel Ryder House
Townsend Drive
Attleborough Fields
Nuneaton
Warwickshire
CV11 6XW
Tel: (0870) 606 6606
www.hollandandbarrett.com
*Stores throughout the UK
selling essential oils and dried
herbs and flowers. Online
shopping service available.*

**Meadows Aromatherapy
Products**
Park Farm Oast
Canterbury Road
Boughton Aluph
Ashford
Kent TN25 4EW
Tel: (0845) 060 0123
Fax: (0845) 060 0456
Email: enquiries
    @meadowsaroma.com

www.meadowsaroma.com
*Suppliers of essential oils, base
oils and soapmaking products.*

Neals Yard Remedies
15 Neals Yard
Covent Garden
London
WC2H 9DP
Tel: (020) 7379 7222
www.nealsyardremedies.co.uk
*Suppliers of oils, essential oils,
bottles and jars, herbs and dried
flowers. Branches throughout
the UK. Online shopping service
available.*

William Hodgson & Co
73a London Road
Alderley Edge
Cheshire
SK9 7DY
Tel: (01625) 599111
Fax: (01625) 599222
*Suppliers of base oils, including
coconut, palm and vegetable
oils (minimum 1 kilo quantity).*

SOUTH AFRICA

Aromatic Aromatherapy
Victoria & Alfred Waterfront
(opposite Pick 'n Pay)
Waterfront
Cape Town 8000
Tel: (021) 418 0648
Suppliers of essential oils.

Cagey Bee
Shop 3, 1 Olifants Road
Emmerentia 2195
Tel: (011) 888 6583
Email: hansh@metroweb.co.za
*Stockists of soapmaking
products, moulds, etc.*

Moco Cosmetic Packaging
18 Auret Street
Jeppestown 2094
Tel: (011) 624 3493/4
Fax: (011) 618 3622
Email: moco@absamail.co.za
*Suppliers of high-quality glass
and plastic bottles and jars.*

Parsons Home Appliances
46 Market Square
Kimberley 8301
Tel: (053) 832 9404/5/6/7
Fax: (053) 832 9408/9
Email: info@parsons.co.za
www.parsons.co.za
*Stockists of soapmaking
products and soap moulds.*

AUSTRALIA

AquaSapone
110 Translator Rd, Armidale
NSW 2350
Tel: (02) 6772 0300
Fax: (02) 781 998-8427
www.aquasapone.com.au
*Suppliers of soapmaking
products and moulds and
essential oils.*

Aussie Soap Supplies
Tel: (08) 9339 1885
Email: heyjude@iinet.com.au
www.aussiesoapsupplies.com.au
*Suppliers of soapmaking raw
materials, oils and containers.*

Australian Botanical Products
36 Meleveton Drive
Hallam Vic 3803
Tel: (03) 9796 4833
Fax: (03) 9796 4966
www.essentialoils.com.au
*Stockists of aromatherapy oils,
soapmaking products and a
range of containers.*

Heirloom Body Care
78 Barnes Road
Llandilo
NSW 2747
Tel: (02) 4777 4457
Fax: (02) 4777 4457
Email: heirloom
   @heirloombodycare.com.au
www.heirloombodycare.com.au
*Suppliers of soapmaking raw
materials, oils, fragrances and
glassware.*

Luscious Skin Care
19 Belltrees Close,
Glen Alpine
NSW 2560
Tel: (02) 4626 7822
Fax: (02) 4626 4777
Email:linfo
   @lusciousskincare.com
www.lusciousskincare.com.au
*Suppliers of carrier and essential
oils and bottles and jars.*

NEW ZEALAND

Aromatherapy New Zealand
Ltd
PO Box 47 470
Ponsonby
Auckland
Tel: (64) 523 5969
www.aroma.co.nz
*Suppliers of a wide range of
essential oils.*

Aromatics & More Ltd
9 Trading Place
Henderson
PO Box 37
Waitakere, Auckland
Tel: (64) 9 835 4330
www.aromaticsandmore.com
*Suppliers of soapmaking
supplies, essential oils,
fragrances and packaging
materials.*

**FURTHER READING AND
USEFUL WEBSITES**

The Practice of Aromatherapy,
   Dr Jean Valnet,
   The CW Daniel Company Ltd

Aromatherapy: An A-Z
   Patricia David
   The CW Daniel Company Ltd

www.thesoapopera.co.uk

www.thesoapkitchen.co.uk

INDEX